STAR WARS®

POWER OF THE FORCE

STAR WARS®

POWER OF THE FORCE

WRITTEN BY ELIZABETH DOWSETT AND SHARI LAST

CONTENTS

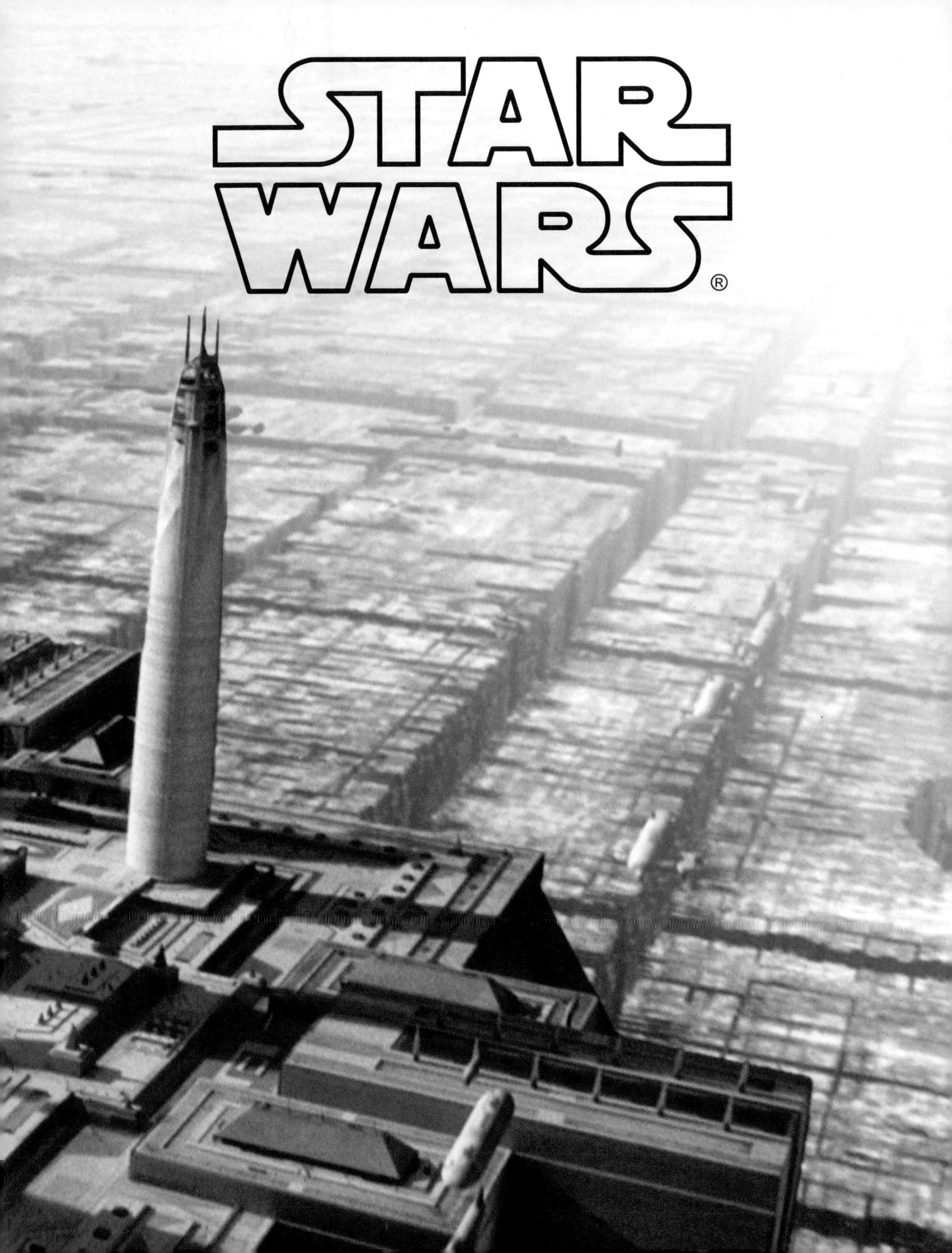
STAR WARS®

■ The Jedi value wisdom very highly. Throughout the book, look out for pieces of Jedi wisdom in special boxes like these.

Dark powers threaten the galaxy and force the Jedi into the Clone Wars. Dark days follow when Sith Lord Darth Sidious, posing as Chancellor of the Republic, takes over the galaxy and makes himself Emperor. But all is not lost. Where there is a Jedi, there is hope...

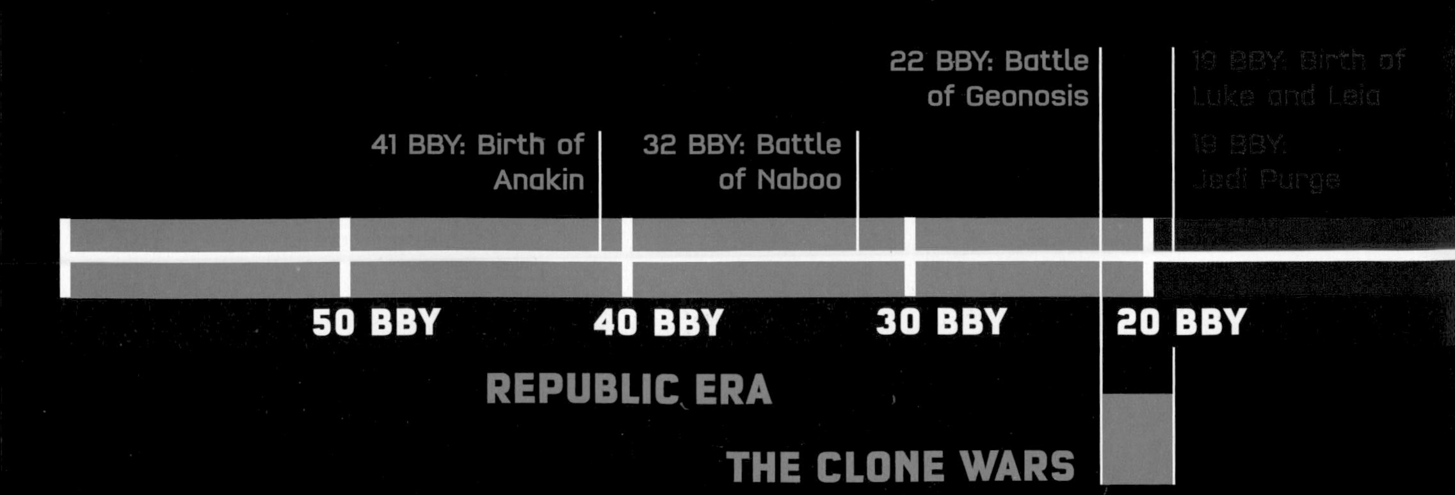

THE JEDI

The word Jedi is known throughout the galaxy. It carries respect and wonder. Mention of the Jedi conjures up images of noble defenders of peace and justice, selfless heroes who put the Republic before themselves.

Despite the popularity of the Jedi, however, little is actually known about the inner workings of this ancient Order. Who exactly are these powerful knights? How do they use a kind of mystical energy known as the Force? How do you become a Jedi and what is it like to dedicate your life to a higher purpose? Welcome to the mysteries of the Jedi...

NOTE ON DATES: Dates are fixed around the Battle of Yavin in year 0. All events prior to this are measured in terms of years Before the Battle of Yavin (BBY). Events after it are measured in terms of years After the Battle of Yavin (ABY).

0 Battle of Yavin

3 ABY: Battle of Hoth

2 BBY: Rebel Alliance is founded

4 ABY: Battle of Endor

10 BBY | 0 | 10 ABY | 20 ABY

According to the Rule of Two, only two Sith can exist at once, a Master and an apprentice. Darth Sidious and his apprentice, Darth Vader, have embarked on a plan to build the most ambitious and terrifying weapon the galaxy has ever seen... the Death Star.

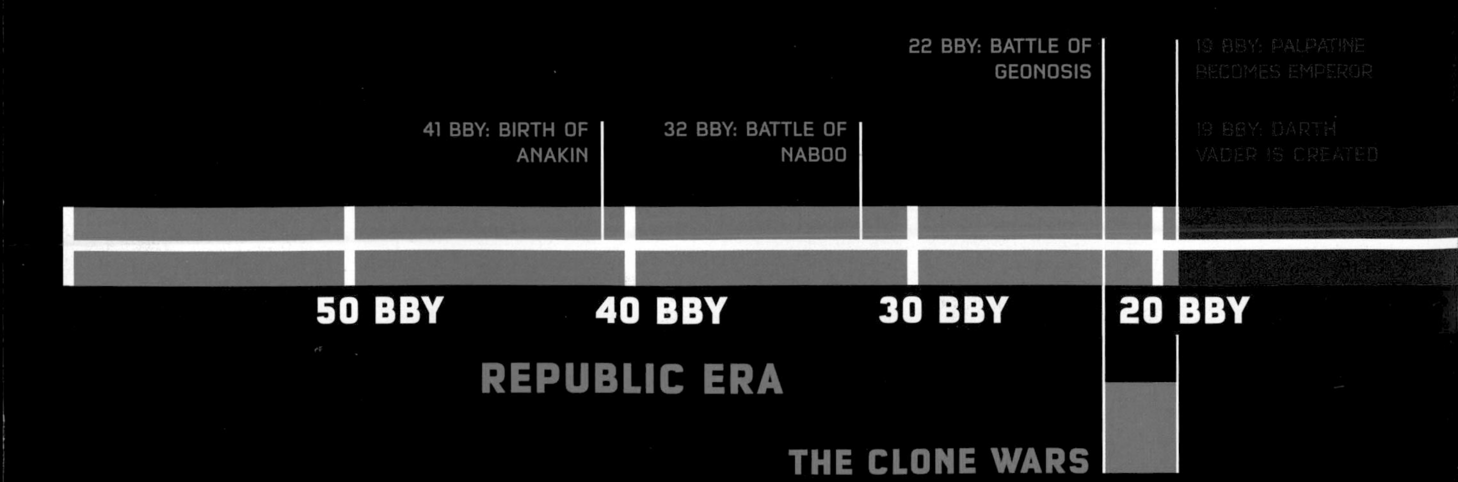

THE SITH

The mere mention of the word "Sith" spreads a ripple of fear across the galaxy. But who are the Sith? What do they want – and how far are they prepared to go to obtain it?

The Sith are an ancient group of Force-sensitive beings who study the dark side of the Force and are known to possess incredible power – but everything else about them is shrouded in secrecy.

Now, for the first time, you will uncover some of the secrets of the Sith. But beware! If you are not careful, you may find yourself unable to resist the power of the dark side...

THE FORCE HAS TWO SIDES

THE FORCE IS AN invisible energy that flows through all living things. Studying the Force will grant you knowledge and power. You must use this power wisely, or face the consequences.

THE LIGHT SIDE

The Jedi study the light side of the Force and use their wisdom to uphold justice and protect the innocent. Using the Force allows Jedi to live in harmony with the galaxy, feel things before they see them, react quickly to danger, and use a lightsaber with incredible skill.

- **BRAVERY**
- **WISDOM**
- **LOYALTY**
- **INNER STRENGTH**
- **JUSTICE**

PASSION

FORBIDDEN KNOWLEDGE

FREEDOM

GREAT STRENGTH

RAW POWER

THE DARK SIDE

The Sith study the dark side of the Force, which feeds on negative feelings such as anger, fear, and jealousy. The dark side offers almost unlimited power and access to dangerous knowledge, but at a terrible price. Submitting to the dark side transforms the Sith into something so evil, they cease to be human.

WHICH WOULD YOU CHOOSE?

FORCE JUMP

CHANNEL THROUGH: Full body
BEST FOR: Leaping out of harm's way; quick movement during a duel; surprising enemies from a great height.
LEARN FROM: Yoda, who evades his enemies during a duel with multiple Force jumps.
DANGER LEVEL: Moderate

The Force might be invisible, but it can be channeled through a Jedi's body for a range of different results.

FORCE DEFLECTION

CHANNEL THROUGH: Hands
BEST FOR: Shielding yourself from incoming attacks.
LEARN FROM: Yoda, who repulses deadly Sith lightning fired at him by Chancellor Palpatine.
DANGER LEVEL: High

FORCE PILOTING

CHANNEL THROUGH: Hands and eyes
BEST FOR: Steering through busy airways.
LEARN FROM: Anakin, who flies safely at super speed above Coruscant.
DANGER LEVEL: High

FEEL THE FORCE

THE FORCE IS AN ENERGY FIELD that flows through every living thing and is accessible to those with the right mindset and training. Jedi spend many years studying how to apply its many uses without causing harm to themselves or others. Do you seek advice? Are you being attacked? The Force can help.

TELEKINESIS

CHANNEL THROUGH: Hands
BEST FOR: Moving objects without touching them; summoning your lightsaber.
LEARN FROM: Yoda, who uses the Force to stop heavy objects from crushing himself and others during his battle with Count Dooku.
DANGER LEVEL: Moderate

FORCE GHOST

CHANNEL THROUGH: Spirit
BEST FOR: Living on after death to advise and guide others.
LEARN FROM: Obi-Wan, who becomes one with the Force after sacrificing himself on the Death Star.
DANGER LEVEL: Low, but only possible for a few rare Jedi.

BEAST CONTROL

CHANNEL THROUGH: Hands and mind
BEST FOR: Taming wild beasts that threaten your safety.
LEARN FROM: Anakin, who takes control of a particularly vicious reek in the execution arena on Geonosis.
DANGER LEVEL: High

FORCE DISTURBANCE

CHANNEL THROUGH: Heart and mind
BEST FOR: Sensing disturbances in the Force; letting you know what is happening elsewhere in the galaxy.
LEARN FROM: Yoda, who senses the start of the Jedi Purge.
DANGER LEVEL: Low

JEDI MIND TRICK

CHANNEL THROUGH: Hands and mind
BEST FOR: Persuading others to leave you alone or to do what you want.
LEARN FROM: Obi-Wan, who convinces a stormtrooper patrol to let him pass through a checkpoint at Mos Eisley.
DANGER LEVEL: Low, but mind tricks work only on the weak-minded. A Jedi must be very careful not to abuse this power.

SMALL BUT STRONG

Never underestimate Yoda! Being small doesn't mean he can't be deadly. Yoda's strength comes from the Force. He achieves any height he needs in battle thanks to acrobatic Force jumps. When Count Dooku realizes that Yoda is more than a match for him, he flees in his Solar Sailer.

Yoda is an immensely powerful Jedi who can control blue crackling Force lightning. It is a cruel weapon of the Sith so he never normally sees it. But he knows that sometimes you must destroy your enemy with their own weapons.

YODA

Yoda is Grand Master of the Jedi Council. He shoulders the great responsibility of leading the Jedi Order. Famous for his unmatched wisdom, Yoda has a strong connection with the Force and often turns to it for answers.

JEDI STATS

SPECIES: UNKNOWN

HOMEWORLD: CORUSCANT

BIRTHDATE: 896 BBY

HEIGHT: 66 CM (2 FT 2 IN)

RANK: JEDI GRAND MASTER

TRAINED BY: UNKNOWN

WEAPON: GREEN-BLADED LIGHTSABER

PREFERRED COMBAT STYLE: FORM IV (ATARU)

TRADEMARK: WISDOM

SMALL HILT FOR SMALL HANDS

SIMPLE, COARSE ROBES

JEDI GUIDE

Yoda is a talented teacher. For generations he has been educating Jedi so that they have the right knowledge, skills, and, most importantly, attitude. He may be in hiding on the swampy planet Dagobah, but that doesn't stop Yoda from passing his knowledge on one last time—to Luke Skywalker.

YOUNG AT HEART

At almost 900 years old, Yoda has seen many changes and known many fine Jedi. He may walk with a stick, but appearances can be deceptive. Not only is Yoda able to leap and spin energetically during a duel, but he also has a rather mischievous sense of humor.

HOW DOES YODA FIGHT SOMEONE SO MUCH BIGGER THAN HIM?

YODA KNOWS THAT size matters not. The aged Jedi Grand Master is a skilled lightsaber warrior who can leap high and fight hard. When he takes on Darth Sidious in the Senate building on Coruscant, Yoda proves that his strength and power have nothing to do with his size.

Yoda's knowledge of the Force makes him just as powerful as Darth Sidious. He can absorb Sidious's Force lightning—and deflect it back! Concentration, focus, and a deep connection with the Force are all Yoda needs in a fight.

Being small can be a definite advantage in some circumstances. Yoda is able to make a quick exit when he escapes through a ventilation shaft.

THE JEDI CODE

Welcome to the Jedi Order. As a Jedi you will learn to harness great power—but you must never use it for personal gain. To live the life of a Jedi, you will need to follow the Jedi Code. It explains the path you must take to become powerful yet remain selfless. The Jedi way of life rests on three basic principles: self-discipline, knowledge, and the Force.

SELF-DISCIPLINE

Your role as a Jedi must come before your own desires. That means having no possessions and not becoming emotionally attached: If a Jedi cares more for something or someone than he does about his mission, he might make a poor decision and jeopardize the safety of the galaxy.

THE FORCE

A Jedi must study the Force and live in tune with it. You must be able to control the Force, communicate with it, and know its will. When you interact with the Force, you will possess great power. But you must use it wisely.

KNOWLEDGE

As a Jedi, you will value knowledge and wisdom in yourself and others. You must learn how to distinguish truth from lies, and how to seek out information so you can solve problems and resolve conflict.

**"THERE IS NO EMOTION, THERE IS PEACE.
THERE IS NO IGNORANCE, THERE IS KNOWLEDGE.
THERE IS NO PASSION, THERE IS SERENITY.
THERE IS NO CHAOS, THERE IS HARMONY.
THERE IS NO DEATH, THERE IS THE FORCE."**

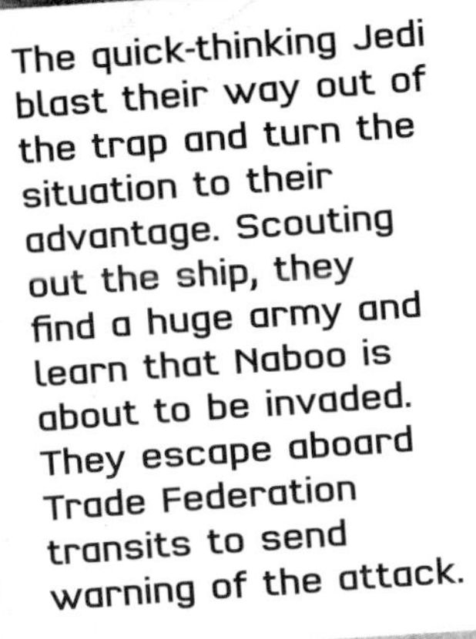

The quick-thinking Jedi blast their way out of the trap and turn the situation to their advantage. Scouting out the ship, they find a huge army and learn that Naboo is about to be invaded. They escape aboard Trade Federation transits to send warning of the attack.

■ The Trade Federation is an organization that supports business across the galaxy. It is not normally violent, but it has come under the control of the Sith Lord Darth Sidious.

WHAT HAPPENS WHEN NEGOTIATIONS FAIL?

JEDI SEEK PEACE THROUGH discussion and reason, but sometimes actions speak louder than words. Qui-Gon Jinn and Obi-Wan Kenobi arrive on a Trade Federation transport on a diplomatic mission to negotiate a solution to the Naboo blockade crisis. However, it is a trap. Before they are even able to enter talks, the two Jedi are attacked. Having sensed all was not well with the Force, they are quick to respond, defending themselves against battle droids and droidekas.

HOW CAN YOU BECOME A JEDI?

Not everyone can become a Jedi: It requires dedication, hard work, and a sensitivity to the Force. It can take more than 20 years of training and there are several stages to go through. If you show promise and are selected, your Jedi career starts here. Good luck!

YOUNGLING

YOUNGLING

Great news! You have been selected to train as a Jedi. You will start as a Youngling and will live in the Jedi Temple, where you will study the basics of the Force. Most Jedi begin their training when they are babies, but some successful Jedi have started later. Get ready to work hard!

JEDI COUNCIL

The Jedi Council is made up of 12 Jedi, who are in charge of running the Jedi Order. They resolve disputes, make decisions, and uphold the Jedi Code.

GRAND MASTER YODA

GRAND MASTER

You'll have to be right at the top of your game to reach this rank. As Grand Master, Yoda is the head of not just the Jedi High Council, but the whole Order. Along with other Council members, he selects who will become Younglings.

JEDI WISDOM

■ Traditionally, those not chosen as Padawans by the age of 13 move into areas like agriculture or medicine. However, the perils of the Clone Wars force the Jedi to take on older Padawans.

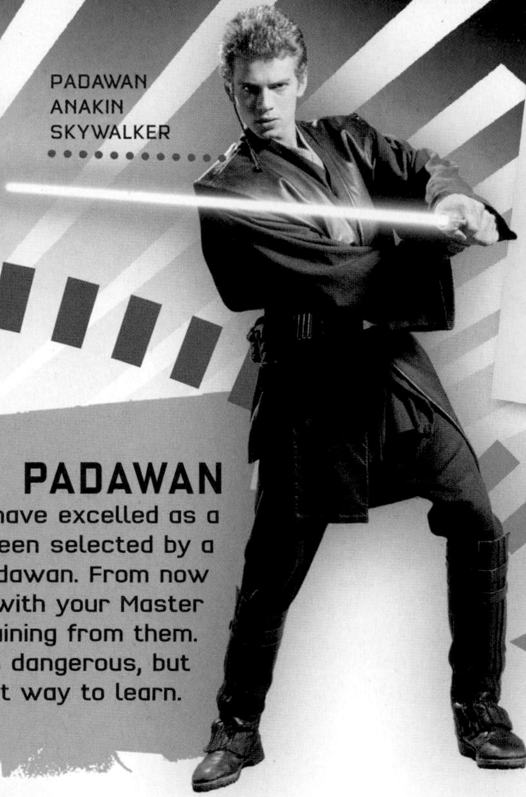

PADAWAN ANAKIN SKYWALKER

JEDI TRIALS

When your Master thinks you have finished your training as a Padawan, you will sit the Jedi Trials. These grueling tasks will push you to your limits to prove you are ready for Jedi Knighthood.

PADAWAN

Well done! You have excelled as a Youngling and have been selected by a Jedi to be their Padawan. From now on, you will travel with your Master and get one-to-one training from them. Going on missions is dangerous, but it's the best way to learn.

JEDI KNIGHT AAYLA SECURA

JEDI KNIGHT

Congratulations! You must have shown great courage and strength in the Jedi Trials because you passed and are a qualified Jedi Knight. Now you can go on your own missions and even train your own Padawan.

JEDI MASTER LUMINARA UNDULI

JEDI MASTER

Once you have trained your own Padawan, you may be promoted to Jedi Master. As a Master, you will continue the duties of a Jedi and can choose another Padawan. If you show exceptional devotion and skill, you may be invited to sit on the Jedi High Council—a great honor.

WHY SHOULD A PADAWAN LISTEN TO HIS MASTER?

Anakin's impulsive attack gives Count Dooku the chance to overpower him and Obi-Wan easily. Anakin's haste also costs him his arm when Dooku's lightsaber slices it off.

Yoda arrives just in time to save Obi-Wan and Anakin, but Dooku escapes, taking with him plans for a superweapon called the Death Star. The Jedi miss the chance to learn more about their mysterious Sith enemy, to end the Clone Wars before they have really begun, and to prevent the building of the Death Star, partially because Anakin failed to heed Obi-Wan.

JEDI IN TRAINING do not study only in safe classrooms. They face real cases of life and death, with only the experience and wisdom of their Masters to guide them. When Obi-Wan and Anakin face Count Dooku, Obi-Wan knows they should fight him together. But the Padawan's anger makes him rush to attack the Sith.

WHO TAUGHT **WHO?**

LEARNING THE JEDI ARTS isn't easy! Every young Padawan is teamed up with a Jedi Master who shares his or her wisdom and experience with them. For centuries, skills have been passed from generation to generation as Padawans become Masters and then take on their own Padawans.

THE JEDI ▸

Ki-Adi-Mundi

Ki-Adi-Mundi began Jedi training at the age of four, which was considered late. However, thanks to his skill, dedication, and guidance from Yoda, he caught up with his peers and became a good Jedi.

YODA

Yoda has been training Jedi for centuries. This natural teacher is dedicated to helping those who want to learn, but he expects complete commitment from them in return. He is quick to point out a student's shortcomings, but also offers guidance on how to overcome them.

Count Dooku

Count Dooku often expressed controversial ideas about the Jedi Order. After his training with Master Yoda, Dooku passed on his unconventional views to his own Padawan, the young Qui-Gon Jinn.

THE SITH ▸

DARTH SIDIOUS

Darth Maul

From a young age, Darth Maul was trained as Sidious's Apprentice in secret. He revealed his existence to the Jedi, which eventually led to his death.

DARTH PLAGUEIS

Sith also follow a Master/pupil system, but the Rule of Two states there may be only two Sith at a time. When Darth Sidious murdered his Master, the mysterious Darth Plagueis, he then searched for his own Apprentice.

Not all teachings begin with Yoda. There are many strands of Masters and Padawans. They represent ancient lines of Jedi wisdom that are still being passed on today. Here are just a few.

CLOSE BONDS

It is an honor to pass on your skills to young Jedi. However, it's not always easy. Masters don't just teach Padawans facts, they must mold their characters with Jedi values, develop their skills, and take care of them in dangerous situations. In these intense relationships, Jedi often form strong bonds that last beyond training.

Qui-Gon Jinn

Qui-Gon was rebellious and outspoken, but he was loyal to the Jedi Order—unlike his former Master, Count Dooku. Qui-Gon's Padawan, Obi-Wan Kenobi, often disagreed with Qui-Gon's opinions, but he also respected Qui-Gon's wisdom and skill.

Obi-Wan Kenobi

At first Obi-Wan struggled to find a Master due to his rash temperament. However, thanks to Qui-Gon's patience and guidance, Obi-Wan became a model Jedi. As Qui-Gon was dying, he made Obi-Wan promise to train Anakin Skywalker.

Anakin Skywalker

Anakin and Obi-Wan developed a very close bond, even though Anakin didn't always agree with his Master. Anakin was often difficult and stubborn, so when he was assigned a Padawan he was given someone equally as stubborn. Anakin learned a lot about teaching when he trained Ahsoka Tano.

Ahsoka Tano

Ahsoka was proud to be Anakin's Padawan. Although their strong personalities clashed at first, they went on to develop a great relationship.

Luke Skywalker

Under the Empire, after the Jedi Purge, the Jedi arts were at risk of being lost. Through Luke, they were preserved and went on to flourish.

Darth Tyranus

For his next Apprentice, Darth Sidious chose the Jedi Count Dooku. He tempted him over to the dark side with promises of great power. Dooku took the Sith name Darth Tyranus, but was ultimately betrayed by Sidious to make way for his next Apprentice, Darth Vader.

Darth Vader

Darth Sidious set his sights on another Jedi for his next Apprentice—Anakin Skywalker. Anakin eventually turned to the dark side and took the name Darth Vader.

MECHANICALLY MINDED
From an early age, Anakin had a knack for seeing how things work. He often tinkered with gadgets for fun. Without being taught, he built his own protocol droid, called C-3PO, from spare parts.

PADAWAN BRAID

LEATHER SURCOAT OVER TUNIC

TALENTED

Anakin has the ability to become a great Jedi. He is brave, heroic, and dedicated, and has a strong sense of justice. Yet he struggles to control his emotions in the way a Jedi should. Sometimes he is impulsive and acts out of anger, revenge, or pride, which gets him into trouble.

JEDI STATS

SPECIES: HUMAN
HOMEWORLD: TATOOINE
BIRTHDATE: 41 BBY
HEIGHT: 1.85 M (6 FT)
RANK: JEDI KNIGHT
TRAINED BY: OBI-WAN KENOBI
WEAPON: BLUE-BLADED LIGHTSABER
PREFERRED COMBAT STYLE: FORM V (SHIEN/DJEM SO)
KNOWN FOR: HEROIC FEATS

Anakin's fighting style uses strong, powerful attacks. As a Padawan, however, he underestimates Count Dooku—which costs him his arm.

Anakin SKYWALKER

As a young boy, Anakin discovers that he is the Chosen One who will bring balance to the Force. But prophecies do not always play out as expected. Anakin has the potential to be the most skilled Jedi ever known, but only he can determine his future.

SHOW-OFF
Anakin is good at being a Jedi—and he knows it. He likes proving that he is better than his Master Obi-Wan, whether he's finding a better way to catch an assassin or flying super fast.

HOW CAN A HUMAN SURVIVE A PODRACE?

JEDI WISDOM

■ Some aliens are good Podracers because they have super-fast reflexes, but it doesn't mean they have the other skills needed to be a Jedi.

Anakin has a talent for understanding how things work. He even built his own Podracer. When it gets damaged, he can fix it himself in mid-air, without having to leave the race.

Podracers don't always play fair—they sometimes try to win by smashing each other's vehicles to pieces. Anakin uses the Force to stay calm and focus on the race so he is unfazed by the attacks from his fiercest competitor, Sebulba.

PODRACING ON TATOOINE is so dangerous that even the best racers are lucky to survive. It's too fast for humans, but Anakin Skywalker is no ordinary human—he has Jedi reflexes. His ability with the Force means he can navigate every swerve and tight corner of the Boonta Eve Classic Podrace, all at super-high speeds. Not only does he survive; he wins!

Practice for the Trial of Skill begins at a young age in classes at the Jedi Temple.

TRIAL OF SKILL

The JEDI

The Jedi Trials are an occasion to prove that you are ready to become a Jedi Knight after years of grueling study.

• FOCUS • KNOWLEDGE • INTELLIGENCE

TRIAL OF SKILL

Simply repeating what you have learned in class will not get you through the Trial of Skill. You must be able to demonstrate that you can apply your complex knowledge, values, and skills under pressure and in different situations.

TRIAL OF FLESH

Brace yourself. As a Jedi, you will have to endure physical and emotional pain and suffer extremes of hunger, heat, and cold. In the Trial of Flesh, you must prove you can rise above these hardships and focus your thoughts elsewhere.

• DETACHMENT • ENDURANCE • STRENGTH

TRIAL OF FLESH

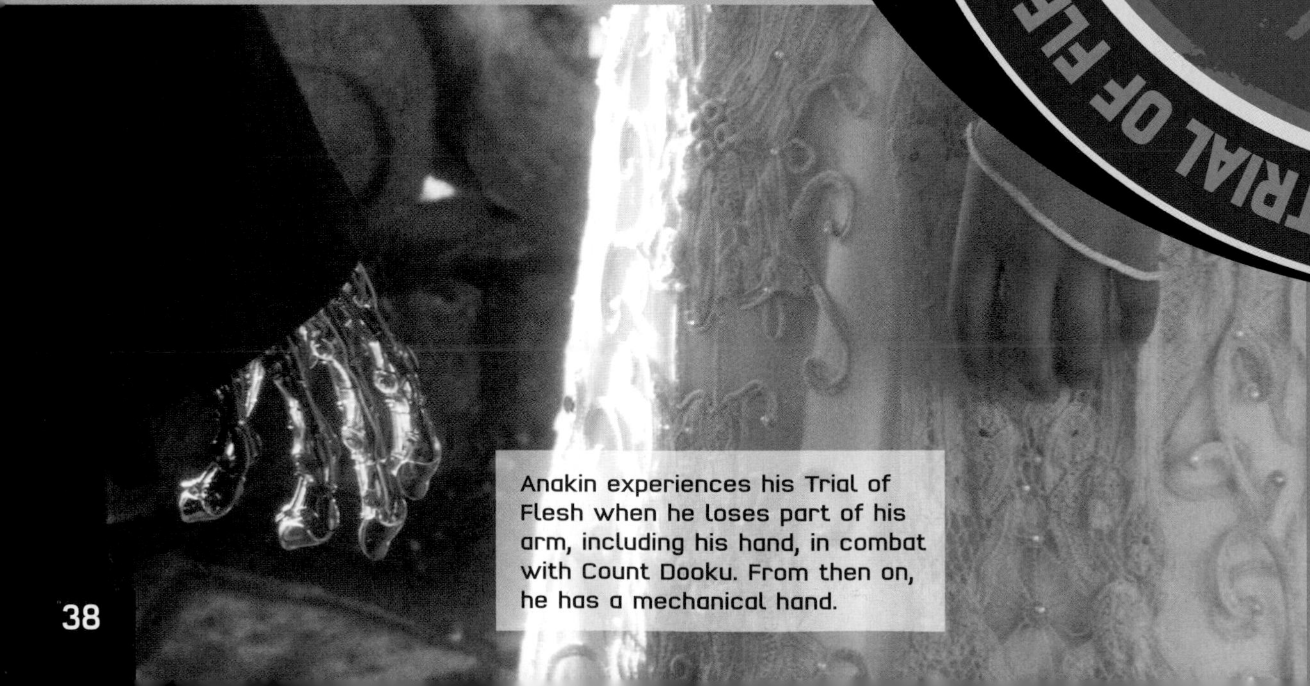

Anakin experiences his Trial of Flesh when he loses part of his arm, including his hand, in combat with Count Dooku. From then on, he has a mechanical hand.

Obi-Wan shows bravery worthy of a Trial of Courage when he takes on Darth Maul in one-to-one combat.

TRIAL OF COURAGE

TRIALS

The four trials are not easy. They are designed to push you to—and beyond—your physical, mental, and emotional limits.

• BRAVERY • COMBAT SKILLS • VALOR

TRIAL OF COURAGE

Facing death is all in a day's work for a Jedi. You must be able to control your fear and channel it into useful actions. The Trial of Courage separates those who dare from those who dare not.

TRIAL OF SPIRIT

Being a Jedi is not just a job—it's a state of mind. You must meditate on who you are and check that your motivations are pure. The Trial of Spirit forces you to look deep inside yourself and address any weaknesses or shortcomings.

• MASTERY OF EMOTIONS • LOYALTY
• MEDITATION

TRIAL OF SPIRIT

On Dagobah, Luke undergoes his Trial of Spirit in a vision where he battles Darth Vader. He struggles with his own dark powers, and fails. Will he turn to the dark side?

Qui-Gon JINN

A Jedi needs to be very skilled with a lightsaber, but also lucky. Qui-Gon's luck runs out against the Sith Lord Darth Maul, but he meets his death valiantly.

MAVERICK

Qui-Gon is quick to speak his mind. He believes in the Jedi way, but his interpretation of it sometimes brings him into conflict with the Jedi Council. This rebellious streak has cost him a seat on the Council. However, Qui-Gon is not interested in politics; he prefers to be true to himself.

TWO-HANDED GRIP FOR PRECISION

Qui-Gon is a wise and powerful Jedi Master. He follows the values of the Jedi Code, but is not afraid to think for himself. He is very conscious of the living Force and is mindful of its will. Qui-Gon likes to live in the moment and focus on the present.

JEDI STATS

SPECIES: HUMAN
HOMEWORLD: UNKNOWN
BIRTHDATE: 92 BBY
HEIGHT: 1.93 M (6 FT 4 IN)
RANK: JEDI MASTER
TRAINED BY: COUNT DOOKU
WEAPON: GREEN-BLADED LIGHTSABER
PREFERRED COMBAT STYLE: FORM IV (ATARU)
TRADEMARK: MAVERICK

ALL HEART

Qui-Gon has a compassionate nature that often spurs him to go beyond the call of duty to help others. On Naboo, he speaks up to save Jar Jar Binks from certain death. In return, the grateful Gungan gives Qui-Gon his loyalty and service, which prove invaluable for the Jedi during the Battle of Naboo.

WELL-WORN JEDI ROBE

LONG HAIR IS A SIGN OF HIS REBELLIOUS NATURE

DETERMINED

Qui-Gon is very self-assured in his opinions. When he finds Anakin on Tatooine, he is convinced that the slave boy is the Chosen One. Qui-Gon is so sure that he risks his own ship in a bet with Anakin's greedy owner, Watto, to win the boy's freedom. He also insists that Anakin be trained as a Jedi, even though it goes against the Jedi Council.

WHAT DOES IT TAKE TO DEFEAT A SITH?

Such is Darth Maul's skill with his double-bladed lightsaber, that Qui-Gon and Obi-Wan must both dig deep to duel him. While Obi-Wan is trapped behind a laser door, Qui-Gon falters in the heat of battle and pays the ultimate price.

With his Master slain, Obi-Wan now fights Darth Maul. The Jedi appears to be at the Sith's mercy: hanging over an abyss, his weapon lost. Using his quick thinking, strength, and the element of surprise, Obi-Wan uses the Force to jump high and grab Qui-Gon's lightsaber. He defeats an unsuspecting Maul with one swift blow.

THE SITH ARE FIERCE warriors who wield great power. They have been in hiding for centuries, honing their skills and biding their time. Finally, they reveal themselves to the Jedi. Darth Maul briefly appeared on Tatooine. Now he is on Naboo and it takes two great Jedi to battle him.

YOU CAN TELL A LOT BY A JEDI'S BODY LANGUAGE

JEDI MISSIONS ARE OFTEN highly dangerous and shrouded in secrecy. However, by paying attention to a Jedi's body language and clothing, you may pick up some clues about what they are up to.

HANDS CLASPED

Clasped hands under a cloak cannot reach easily for a weapon. Jedi stand like this on diplomatic missions as a sign of peace, service, and respect.

BLENDING IN

If you spot a Jedi wearing non-Jedi clothes, don't approach him. He is probably on an undercover mission and wants to keep his Jedi identity secret.

HOOD ON

If you see a Jedi with his hood on, don't disturb him—it means he's on a secret mission. A Jedi will wear his hood to help deflect attention when it's not safe for him to be out in the open.

CLOAK OFF

When you see a Jedi discard his or her cloak, get ready for action! Their long cloaks are not practical when fighting; a Jedi needs to be able to move freely.

Luminara UNDULI

Jedi Master Luminara Unduli is a stickler for the rules. As far as she's concerned, there's little room in the Jedi Code for self-expression. For her, the cornerstones of the Jedi Order are discipline, discipline, discipline.

TOUGH TASKMASTER

Luminara expects the same high standards of her Padawan and her troops as she does of herself. She is demanding and strict, but is respected so she gets the best out of people.

JEDI STATS

SPECIES: MIRIALAN
HOMEWORLD: MIRIAL
BIRTHDATE: 58 BBY
HEIGHT: 1.70 M (5 FT 7 IN)
RANK: JEDI MASTER
TRAINED BY: UNKNOWN
PREFERRED COMBAT STYLE: FORM III (SORESU)
TRADEMARK: ADHERENCE TO RULES

HUMBLE ADVISOR

Luminara is a trusted contributor to the Jedi Council, but is mindful of her position. She stands back respectfully and offers her opinion only when asked for it.

FLOWING MIRIALAN ROBES

JEDI STATS

SPECIES: MIRIALAN

HOMEWORLD: MIRIAL

BIRTHDATE: 40 BBY

HEIGHT: 1.66 M (5 FT 5 IN)

RANK: JEDI KNIGHT

TRAINED BY: LUMINARA UNDULI

PREFERRED COMBAT STYLE: FORM III (SORESU)

TRADEMARK: RESPONSIBILITY

A HEALING FORCE

Barriss has a strong connection to the Force. This helps her wield her lightsaber like a pro. But even more valuable in the middle of war, Barriss is an expert at using the Force to heal sick or injured people.

Barriss OFFEE

Barriss Offee is a model Padawan. She is loyal, obedient, and respectful to her strict Master, Luminara Unduli. After earning her knighthood during the Clone Wars, she continues to serve alongside Luminara.

MIRIALAN TATTOOS

STEPPING UP

Barriss is only a Padawan when she is flung into the Clone Wars. Her lightsaber skills and cool head help her rise to meet the challenge.

HOW TO BUILD A LIGHTSABER

THE LIGHTSABER is an ancient sword known for its elegance as well as its power in battle. It is the weapon of choice for both the Jedi and their enemies, the Sith. Lightsabers consist of a handle, or "hilt," that emits a colored blade of plasma energy. As part of their training, every Jedi learns how to build their own lightsaber. All lightsabers contain these eight basic parts, but you can vary the design to suit your own taste and needs.

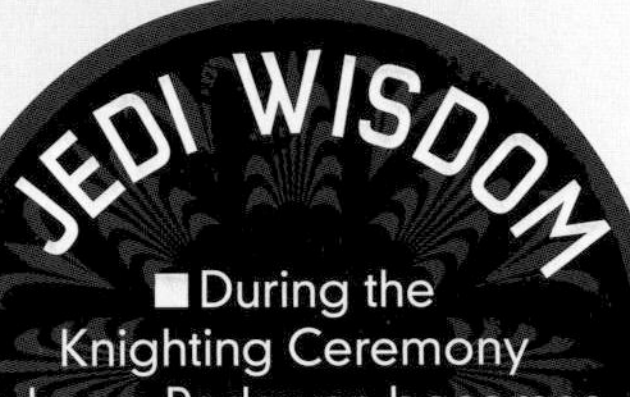

JEDI WISDOM

■ During the Knighting Ceremony when a Padawan becomes a Knight, a lightsaber is used to cut off the Padawan's braid.

MAIN HILT ■

The plasma for the blade is created here in the blade energy channel from a special type of gas.

■ BLADE EMITTER

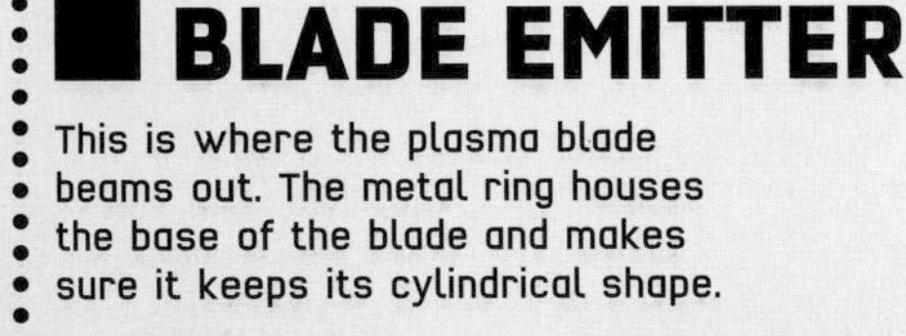

This is where the plasma blade beams out. The metal ring houses the base of the blade and makes sure it keeps its cylindrical shape.

FOCUSING LENS ■

The focusing lens channels the plasma for the blade and makes sure it has a fixed end point. Most blades are one meter (3¼ feet) long, but they can vary.

BLADE ENERGY CHANNEL

CRYSTAL

A crystal sits at the heart of every lightsaber and gives the blade its bright color. Most Jedi lightsabers glow blue or green because they use crystals mined on the planet Ilum. The Sith prefer to make their own artificial crystals so their blades glow a more fearsome red color.

The crystal also determines the length of the blade. Having more than one crystal means you can vary the length of your blade. Many Jedi believe that three is best number of crystals to have.

POWER CELL

Energy from special diatium batteries stored in the power cell heats up gas to create plasma for the blade.

POMMEL CAP

The pommel seals the end of the lightsaber. It often contains a back-up battery. If you want, you can add a ring that clips to your belt.

CONTROLS

Buttons activate the blade, but Jedi who are very skilled in the Force can control these things using the Force instead.

ENERGY GATE

BUTTON ADJUSTS BLADE'S LENGTH

BUTTON ADJUSTS BLADE'S POWER SETTING

HANDGRIP

This outer part of the hilt is covered in ridges so that the lightsaber doesn't fly out of your hand while you are swinging it around.

DOS AND DON'TS

- Don't plunge your blade into water—it will sizzle out unless it has been specially adapted to work underwater.
- Take care of your lightsaber—if you lose it, it can take a month to build a new one.
- Make sure your power cell is covered with an inert power insulator, otherwise you could get electrocuted!
- Keep fit: The forces acting on the weightless blade mean that a lightsaber requires strong arms to control it.
- Study the Force: Anyone can wield a lightsaber, but only those with Force powers can unlock its true potential.
- Be careful: The blade can slice through almost anything. (Any injuries you get won't bleed because the blade is so hot it seals the skin, but that doesn't mean they won't hurt!)
- Keep your lightsaber in good condition and it could last forever and never run out of power.

WHAT HAPPENS WHEN A CYBORG STUDIES JEDI SKILLS?

General Grievous is a fearsome fighter, and his lightsabers make him all the more deadly. But he doesn't understand the Force. Obi-Wan shows him that four lightsabers are no match for one lightsaber wielded by a true Jedi.

Grievous thinks he is better than the Jedi. However, no Jedi thinks himself above anyone. Grievous's arrogance is his downfall. Obi-Wan struggles in their duel, but in the end, his emotional detachment brings him victory.

COUNT DOOKU HAS trained General Grievous in the Jedi arts. These lightsaber skills have made the part-machine, part-organic warrior even more dangerous. However, just being able to wield a lightsaber doesn't make him a Jedi. Not that he wants to be a Jedi: Grievous likes nothing better than killing Jedi and adding their lightsabers to his creepy collection.

JEDI WISDOM

■ General Grievous was a reptilian Kaleesh warrior who was injured in battle. Now all that remains of his body are his brain and the organs encased in his metal chest.

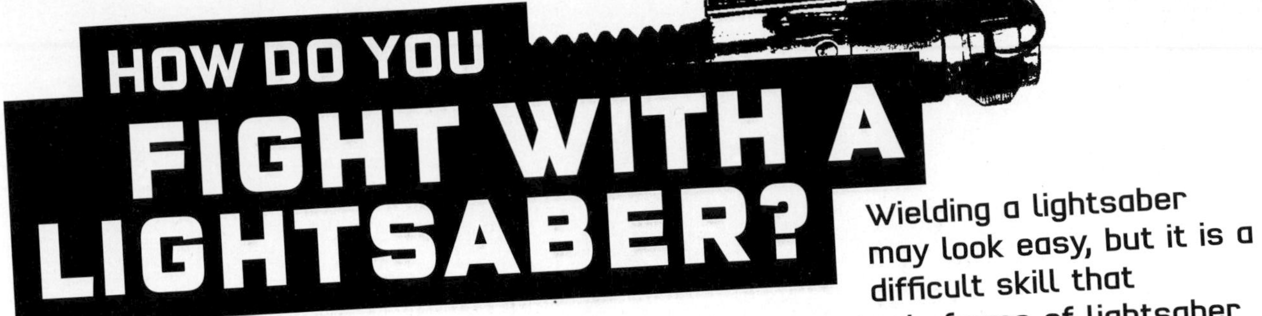

HOW DO YOU FIGHT WITH A LIGHTSABER?

Wielding a lightsaber may look easy, but it is a difficult skill that requires much training. There are seven main forms of lightsaber combat. Every Jedi has a favorite, but the most skilled can switch between all the styles depending on the situation.

TRAINING HELMET

SHII-CHO BASIC STANCE

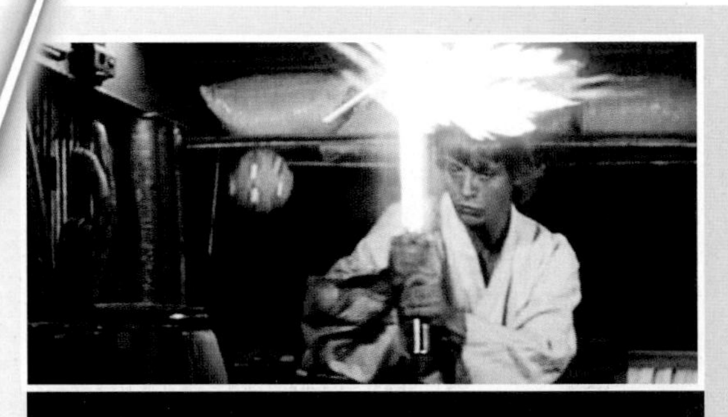

Luke begins with Shii-Cho as a way of learning to channel the Force and master his lightsaber. This exercise involves deflecting blasts from a training remote.

FORM I: SHII-CHO

When trainee Jedi get their lightsabers, the first thing they learn is Form I. It introduces them to all the basic parts of lightsaber combat: how to attack and how to defend or "parry." To master it properly, Younglings practice all the steps again and again in drills known as "velocities."

ALSO KNOWN AS: Way of the Sarlacc or Determination Form

FORM II: MAKASHI

Makashi is a development of Shii-Cho that is designed for lightsaber-to-lightsaber duels. Precision and discipline are key to Makashi, rather than strength or power. The style requires very accurate bladework and elegant, well-balanced footwork.

ALSO KNOWN AS: Way of the Ysalamir or Contention Form

Count Dooku's calm and measured moves make him a master of Makashi. However, the form lacks great power and Dooku meets his match against the force of Anakin Skywalker's style.

MAKASHI OPENING SALUTE

BLADE PROTECTS BODY

FORM III: SORESU

For Jedi who find themselves under blaster attack, then Soresu is a good choice. It is the most defensive of the seven forms. The idea is to make only small movements and keep the blade close to the body to give the best protection from blaster fire. Although Soresu is defensive, it does not have to be passive: Jedi sometimes defend themselves until their opponent tires—then they attack.

ALSO KNOWN AS: Way of the Mynock or Resilience Form

On Kamino, Obi-Wan uses Soresu to deflect blaster fire from the bounty hunter Jango Fett.

SORESU BRACE-READY STANCE

FORM IV: ATARU

For agile and athletic Jedi, Ataru is a good option. Masters of this form use acrobatic jumps, twirls, and twists to drive power into their bold attacks. It's also handy for short Jedi like Yoda who want to add height to their reach. Furthermore, it's useful for confusing and distracting your opponent.

ALSO KNOWN AS: Way of the Hawk-Bat or Aggression Form

Obi-Wan uses his mastery of Ataru along with the Force to add great power to his lightsaber moves.

ATARU PRE-JUMP STANCE

FORM V: SHIEN/DJEM SO

The two versions of Form V developed out of Form III to combine aggression with the defensive style. Shien is used for redirecting blaster bolts back at the person who fired them. Djem-So is used to push back another lightsaber during a duel. Whichever a Jedi chooses, they must be strong and fit so their deflective moves really pack a punch.

ALSO KNOWN AS: Way of the Krayt Dragon or Perseverance Form

Anakin is very strong and he uses this power to drive aggression into his Djem So attacks.

DJEM SO OPENING STANCE

FORM VI: NIMAN

Niman is about balance and harmony rather than aggressive power. It is a good choice for Jedi who are less experienced in battle because it is less demanding than the other forms. It covers the basic moves, but is too general for some situations so is often used with other Force powers like telekinesis.

ALSO KNOWN AS: Way of the Rancor or Moderation Form

Niman is very popular during the Battle of Geonosis among Jedi like Joclad Danva.

NIMAN OPENING STANCE

FORM VII: JUYO/VAAPAD

If a Jedi is super-energetic, then the big, direct moves of Form VII could be their best option. But this style comes with a warning: Form VII can be dangerous because it taps into powerful emotions that can open a Jedi up to the dark side. Juyo is the original version. Vaapad is a variant developed by the Jedi Master Mace Windu that particularly focuses on a Jedi's state of mind.

ALSO KNOWN AS: Way of Vornskr or Ferocity Form

VAAPAD OPENING STANCE

Mace is one of the few Jedi strong enough to use dark feelings without falling to the dark side.

Anakin Skywalker's Lightsaber
Mace's hilt is plated with golden electrum metal—a decoration reserved for senior Jedi.
Mace Windu's Lightsaber
Mace chooses a rare crystal that emits a violet glow.
Luke Skywalker's Lightsaber
Youngling Lightsaber
This lightsaber is passed from Anakin to Luke. It is lost when Luke fights Darth Vader on Cloud City.
After Luke loses his first lightsaber fighting Darth Vader, he builds a new one using notes left by Obi-Wan.
Younglings practice with safety blades. The power setting is very low to avoid injuries.
"Your lightsaber is ...YOUR LIFE!"
OBI-WAN TO ANAKIN
The Sith Darth Maul chooses a saberstaff, which is double-bladed. These are harder to use, but some Sith favor them because they look more menacing and allow a more aggressive style of combat.
Darth Maul's Lightsaber

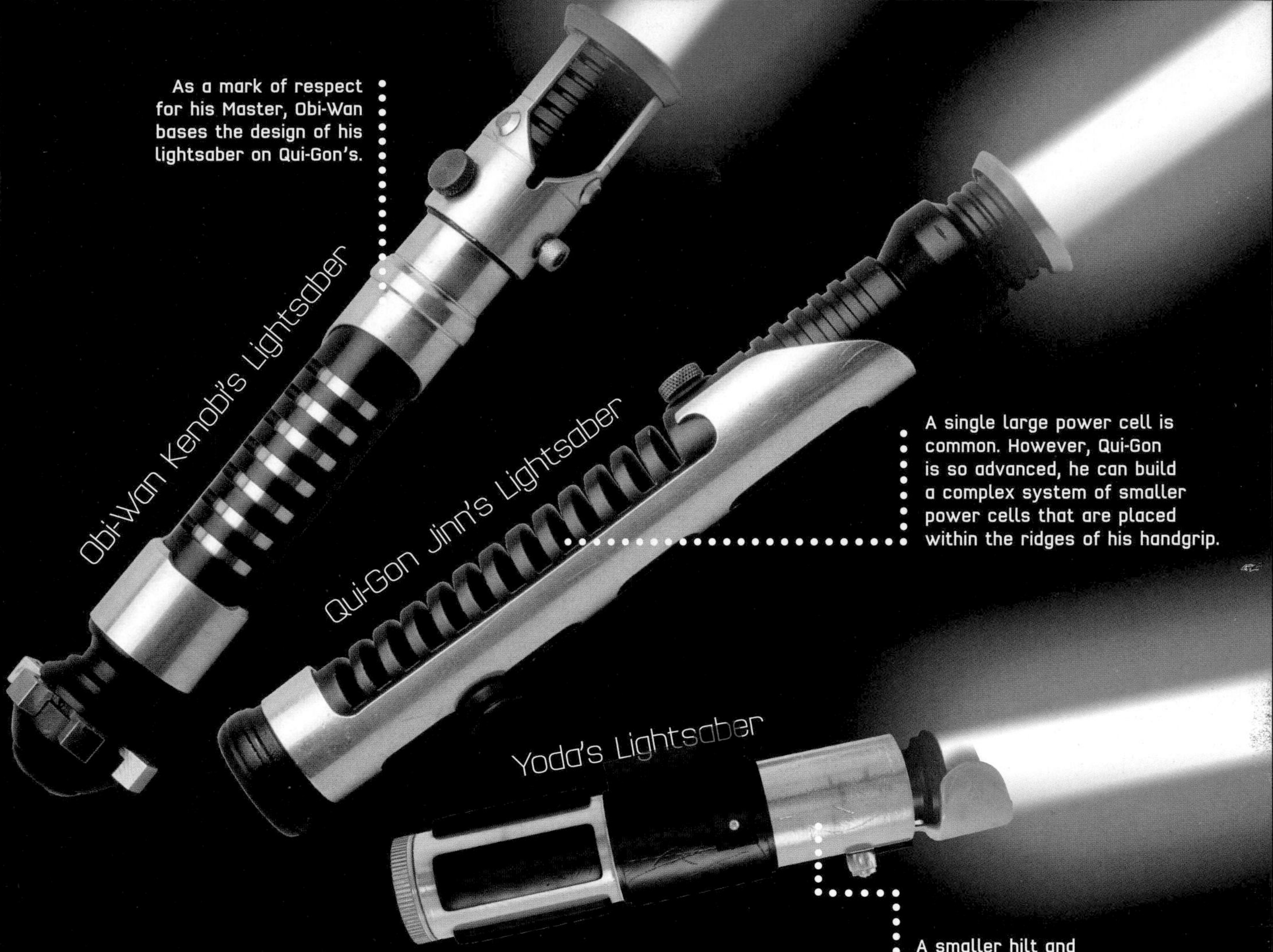

As a mark of respect for his Master, Obi-Wan bases the design of his lightsaber on Qui-Gon's.

Obi-Wan Kenobi's Lightsaber

Qui-Gon Jinn's Lightsaber

A single large power cell is common. However, Qui-Gon is so advanced, he can build a complex system of smaller power cells that are placed within the ridges of his handgrip.

Yoda's Lightsaber

A smaller hilt and shorter blade are perfectly sized for Yoda.

LIGHTSABER SPOTTING

EVERY LIGHTSABER IS handmade by its owner, so there is a dazzling array of variations. A Jedi or Sith can customize the handle, controls, size, and color according to their needs and their tastes.

JEDI WISDOM

■ Jedi lightsabers use natural crystals that usually glow blue or green. The Sith use synthetic crystals which glow red; a more menacing color.

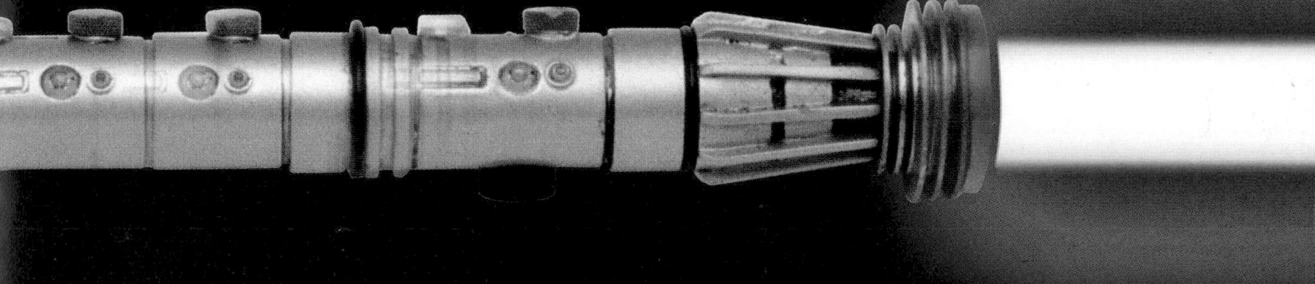

Aayla SECURA

JEDI STATS

SPECIES: TWI'LEK
HOMEWORLD: RYLOTH
BIRTHDATE: UNKNOWN
HEIGHT: 1.78 M (5 FT 10 IN)
RANK: JEDI MASTER
TRAINED BY: QUINLAN VOS & THOLME
PREFERRED COMBAT STYLE: FORM IV (ATARU) & FORM V (SHIEN/DJEM SO)
TRADEMARK: EMPATHY

RUTIAN SKIN COLOR

BRUSH WITH EVIL

Aayla knows first hand what the temptations of the dark side can be. In her youth, she struggled with dark powers, but this has made her stronger. She is a more determined Jedi as a result.

LEKKU (HEAD TAILS) CAN EXPRESS EMOTIONS

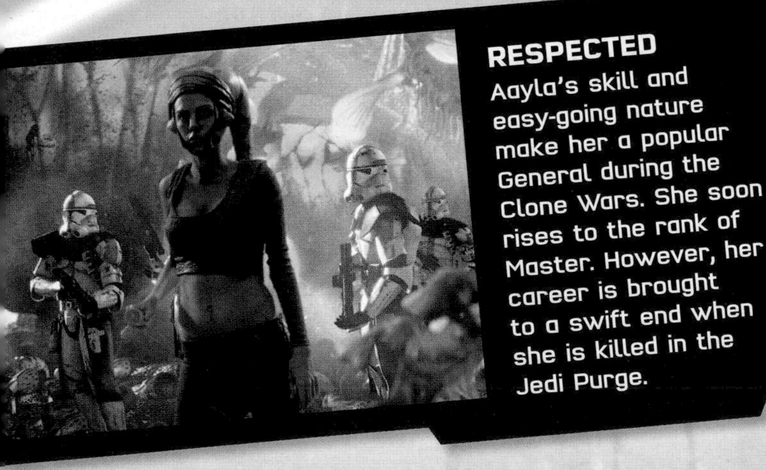

RESPECTED
Aayla's skill and easy-going nature make her a popular General during the Clone Wars. She soon rises to the rank of Master. However, her career is brought to a swift end when she is killed in the Jedi Purge.

Aayla Secura is a talented Twi'lek Jedi with distinctive blue skin. Her quick thinking has saved many lives. She brings a light-hearted and mischievous approach to the serious business of being a Jedi.

KI-ADI-MUNDI

As a Cerean, Ki-Adi-Mundi believes in a simple way of life, and this simplicity serves him well as a Jedi. His large Cerean brain gives him extra thinking power and earns him a well-deserved seat on the Jedi High Council.

LARGE BINARY BRAIN

BODY HAS TWO HEARTS TO SUPPORT LARGE BRAIN

BRAINY GENERAL
The outbreak of the Clone Wars sees Ki-Adi-Mundi's insightful and logical mind put to work on the battlefield. He leads his troops with honor and survives the conflict, only to die in the Jedi Purge.

JEDI STATS

SPECIES: CEREAN
HOMEWORLD: CEREA
BIRTHDATE: 92 BBY
HEIGHT: 1.98 M (6 FT 6 IN)
RANK: JEDI MASTER
TRAINED BY: YODA
PREFERRED COMBAT STYLE: FORM III (SORESU)
TRADEMARK: INTELLIGENCE

FAMILY MAN

Although Jedi are not allowed to marry or have children, a special exception is made for Ki-Adi-Mundi because the Cereans have a very low birthrate. Nevertheless, he always puts his duties as a Jedi ahead of his feelings, even when his family is killed in the Clone Wars.

THE JEDI TEMPLE TOUR

The Jedi Temple stands out on Coruscant thanks to its unique appearance. One of the oldest and largest buildings on the planet, the 4,000-year-old Temple has a huge, pyramid-like base and five colossal spires. It is the headquarters of the Jedi Order. Come, take the Jedi Temple Tour.

COUNCIL OF FIRST KNOWLEDGE TOWER

THE PLANET

Welcome to Coruscant—a planet entirely covered by a single city. You are visiting the place that is the most important political hub in the galaxy, thanks to its central location. Coruscant was the capital city of the Republic, home to the Galactic Senate, the office of the Chancellor, and, of course, the Jedi Temple. During the Emperor's reign, the planet was also home to the Imperial Palace. Enjoy your stay!

SURFACE LIFE

This planet is a bustling metropolis, full of bright lights and congested skylanes. It is home to over 1 trillion residents, made up of a multitude of races and species. Many areas are built up with beautiful, modern architecture—but be warned! A dangerous underworld lurks in the shadows. Watch out for prowling gangs who make some areas unsafe.

TEMPLE SPIRE

JEDI REASSIGNMENT COUNCIL TOWER IS BEHIND THE TEMPLE SPIRE

TOWER OF RECONCILIATION

HIGH COUNCIL TOWER

THE SPIRE

Look up! At the peak of the Temple's southwestern spire you can see the meeting chamber of the Jedi High Council. This airy room has 12 chairs arranged in a circle, allowing the Council members to see each other, and symbolizing that each person's opinion is equally important.

JEDI WISDOM

■ The five spires of the Jedi Temple are topped with powerful antennas that enable communication with Jedi on distant planets throughout the galaxy.

THE TEMPLE

Next stop: the Jedi Temple, home to the Jedi Order. Within these gleaming walls are training rooms, the Jedi Archives, offices, meditation chambers, bedrooms, and the Jedi Council Meeting Chamber. Only a few areas of the Jedi Temple are open to the public.

THE JEDI HIGH COUNCIL

COUNCIL MEMBERS IN 32 BBY

YADDLE
Yaddle contributes wisdom, compassion, and patience to the Council.

SAESEE TIIN
Saesee is particularly valued on the Council for his skill of foresight.

KI-ADI-MUNDI
Ki-Adi-Mundi, Mace, and Yoda are the three most senior Council members.

EVEN PIELL
Even's seriousness makes him well-suited to important Council business.

OPPO RANCISIS
Oppo believes the Council should focus on traditional ideas, not modern ones.

ADI GALLIA
Adi's intuition and network of informants strengthen the Council.

LATER COUNCIL MEMBERS

ANAKIN SKYWALKER
Chancellor Palpatine chooses Anakin to serve as his personal representative on the Council. Palpatine and the Council each want Anakin to spy on the other.

SHAAK TI
The Sith spare Shaak's life so she can report Palpatine's kidnap to the Council.

OBI-WAN KENOBI
Obi-Wan proves himself worthy of a place on the Council during the challenging Clone Wars.

COLEMAN KCAJ
Coleman follows in the footsteps of many Ongree Jedi who have sat on the Council.

YODA

Yoda is the most respected Jedi and leads the High Council.

MACE WINDU

Mace's wisdom meant he joined the Council at the very young age of only 28.

PLO KOON

Plo thinks his friend Qui-Gon Jinn deserves a seat on the Council, but the others find Qui-Gon too unpredictable.

IF YOU PROVE YOURSELF to be among the most skilled and wise Jedi, then you may be given the highest honor—a seat on the Jedi High Council. As a Council member, you will have a role in organizing the Jedi Order. There are always 12 seats and if a member dies or steps down, a new member is selected by the Council to replace them.

DEPA BILLABA

Experiencing the horrors of the Clone Wars causes Depa to turn to the dark side.

YARAEL POOF

Yarael has two brains with which to ponder Council debates.

EETH KOTH

Eeth's intelligence and insight bring clarity to Council discussions.

STASS ALLIE

Before she joined the Council, Stass had a role as an advisor to senior officials in the Republic.

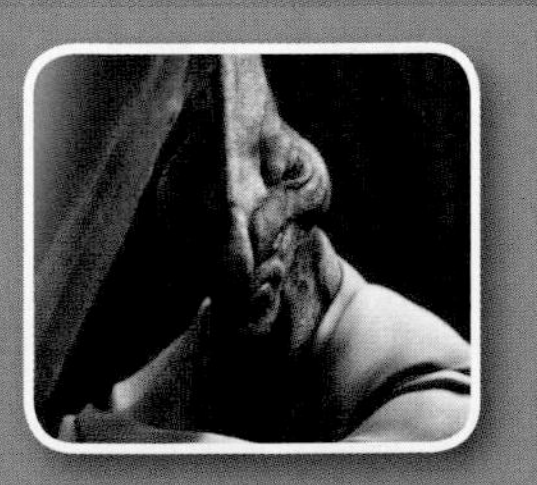

COLEMAN TREBOR

Coleman is media savvy and becomes the spokesperson for the Council.

KIT FISTO

Kit's achievements in the Clone Wars earn him a seat on the Council.

AGEN KOLAR

Agen is very loyal to the Council and, like most Jedi, does not question its decisions.

JEDI WISDOM

■ There are three types of Council membership. Life members commit for life. Long-term members can step down. Limited-term members serve for a fixed period.

JEDI WISDOM

For Jedi, wisdom and knowledge are the keys to success. A mission's outcome can hinge on having the most accurate data available. Gathering information is a never-ending task. Like Obi-Wan, you must ensure your facts are reliable and up-to-date. Here are some tips to guide you on your search.

1. USE THE JEDI ARCHIVES

With its ancient collection of Holocrons and millions of holobooks, the Jedi Archives are the perfect place to start your search for knowledge. Every time a piece of information is learned by the Jedi Order, it is filed and stored in the Archives for future use.

2. DIG DEEP

Always question and analyze your data—don't take anything at face value. Once, Obi-Wan couldn't find the planet Kamino in the Archives' records. Jedi Librarian Jocasta Nu told him that meant Kamino didn't exist. Obi-Wan was not so sure—someone may have tampered with the Archives.

3. GO UNDERCOVER

On the trail of a tricky villain, you might have to improvise. If you can't learn the truth through simple methods, you may have to resort to spying. Obi-Wan tracked Count Dooku to Geonosis where he overheard him discussing his plans for a Death Star.

4. MAKE CONTACTS

Sometimes it's not what you know but who. Some people are happy to talk, but others may want money. You never know who might be useful. When Obi-Wan seeks information about underworld weapons, he goes to his old friend Dexter Jettster.

5. GO THE EXTRA MILE

Sometimes, all the research in the galaxy is not enough. If nobody is willing to talk, you might just have to put in lots of extra effort to get the facts. When Obi-Wan was chasing Zam Wesell for information, he risked his life by speeding through Coruscant's skylanes hanging on to an assassin droid!

Holocrons are mysterious databanks that store the deepest secrets of the Jedi. Unlike simple data files and holobooks, these ancient artifacts can be accessed only by using the Force.

Informatic stations are situated throughout the Jedi Archives. Insert a holobook into the station and it will link up with new data being accessed from all over the galaxy.

Obi-Wan **KENOBI**

Obi-Wan Kenobi is a model Jedi. He is humble, calm, and steadfast, but can be combative when the need arises. Tutored by Qui-Gon, he passes his knowledge on to Anakin Skywalker and, later, to Anakin's son, Luke.

JEDI STATS

SPECIES: HUMAN
HOMEWORLD: STEWJON
BIRTHDATE: 57 BBY
HEIGHT: 1.79 M (5 FT 11 IN)
RANK: JEDI MASTER
TRAINED BY: QUI-GON JINN
WEAPON: BLUE-BLADED LIGHTSABER
PREFERRED COMBAT STYLE: FORM IV (ATARU); LATER FORM III (SORESU)
TRADEMARK: NEGOTIATION

Obi-Wan is an ace with a lightsaber. When he was only a Padawan, he took on Darth Maul and his double-bladed lightsaber—and won.

LAYERED TUNIC

HOODED ROBE

HIGH HOPES

Obi-Wan sees a little of his former self in his Padawan's arrogance and impatience. This makes him believe that he can influence Anakin to be a better Jedi, as his Master, Qui-Gon, did for him.

THE NEGOTIATOR

Obi-Wan is known for his ability to resolve disputes with words and reason. People listen to him because of his charm and skills as a negotiator, but also thanks to his reputation with a lightsaber. These qualities make him a respected General in the Clone Wars.

STANDING FIRM

Obi-Wan is fiercely loyal to the Jedi Order, democracy, and justice. Even when held prisoner by Count Dooku, he refuses to join him. Nothing would make Obi-Wan turn his back on what he believes in.

Amid the chaos of the hurtling rock, clever Obi-Wan fools Jango into thinking that an exploding asteroid is his ship. Believing that he has seen Obi-Wan go up in flames, Jango zooms off, not expecting to see Obi-Wan again.

HOW DO YOU OUTWIT A BOUNTY HUNTER?

JEDI WISDOM

■ Bounty hunters do not fight for an army, but are paid on a job-by-job basis to do tasks like capturing people wanted by the Republic or the Empire.

WHEN A BOUNTY HUNTER is fighting you, he or she will not stop until the job is done and you are captured—or worse. Obi-Wan hates flying at the best of times, but now ruthless Jango Fett is gunning for him. Being a good pilot, and even steering his Delta-7 starfighter into an asteroid belt, is not enough to throw Jango. It requires something much more cunning to outwit him.

DARK SUSPICIONS

Mace has never hit it off with Anakin. Mace's deep connection with the Force means that he can sense Anakin's strong emotional attachments and so he fears for his future. Mace tries to keep Anakin in check, but the more he does this, the more he pushes Anakin away.

Mace never ignores a Jedi in trouble so he is quick to volunteer for the dangerous mission to Geonosis. The daring rescue quickly escalates into full-scale battle, but Mace's skill helps him and his troops to victory.

Mace WINDU

Across the galaxy, Mace Windu is respected for his wisdom and nobility. As a senior member of the Jedi Council, he has heavy burdens to bear. Mace has a deep knowledge of Jedi history and philosophy. When he talks, people listen.

JEDI STATS

SPECIES: HUMAN

HOMEWORLD: HARUUN KAL

BIRTHDATE: 72 BBY

HEIGHT: 1.88 M (6 FT 2 IN)

RANK: JEDI MASTER

TRAINED BY: UNKNOWN

WEAPON: VIOLET-BLADED LIGHTSABER

PREFERRED COMBAT STYLE: FORM VII (JUYO/VAAPAD)

TRADEMARK: STRENGTH

NO PUSHOVER

For Mace, the Jedi are peacekeepers, not soldiers. He likes to spend his time meditating in the Jedi Temple, but that doesn't mean he's a coward. When events force the Jedi into war, Mace is ready to stand up and fight for the things he believes in—the Republic and the Jedi Order.

RARE VIOLET BLADE

GRIP FOR SWIFT ONE-HANDED STRIKES

JEDI UTILITY POUCH

BETRAYED

As a guardian of the Republic, Mace steps up to arrest Chancellor Palpatine when he learns that he is a Sith Lord. The powerful Jedi is capable of defeating Palpatine. However, Mace's misgivings about Anakin return to haunt him. Anakin steps in and Mace dies.

Jedi STARFLEET

Keeping peace across the galaxy requires wings, so piloting is a basic Jedi skill. Jedi use different types of ship depending on the needs of the mission, and some have Force-activated controls.

PRESSURIZED COCKPIT

DELTA-7 STARFIGHTER

- MAIN USE: SCOUT AND PURSUIT

This small, wedge-shaped ship is sleek and fast—ideal for keeping a low profile during enemy pursuit. Obi-Wan pilots one of these streamlined ships on his scout mission to Kamino, making use of its excellent maneuverability when pursuing the bounty hunter Jango Fett.

ANCIENT JEDI SYMBOL

LENGTH: 8 m (26 ft)
HYPERDRIVE RATING: Class 1.0
CAPACITY: 1 person

LENGTH: 5.47 m (18 ft)
HYPERDRIVE RATING: Class 1.0
CAPACITY: 1 person

ETA-2 INTERCEPTOR

- MAIN USE: COMBAT

This compact model is the Jedi ship of choice in the last years of the Republic. Adapted so Jedi pilots could use the Force instead of traditional controls, this lightweight vehicle is fast and agile. It does not have its own internal hyperdrive, so it uses an external booster ring to reach hyperspace.

SECONDARY ION CANNON

WINGS OPEN DURING INTENSE FIGHTING

LONG-BARRELED LASER CANNON

ASTROMECH DROID

FUSIAL ION ENGINE

WINGS OPEN TO MAKE "X" SHAPE

LONG-RANGE LASER CANNON

STREAMLINED HULL

LENGTH: 12.5 m (41 ft)
HYPERDRIVE RATING: Class 1.0
CAPACITY: 1 person

T-65 X-WING

- MAIN USE: COMBAT

When Luke Skywalker fights against the Empire, he flies an X-wing. This long, narrow starship boasts excellent power, balance, and stability.

Proton torpedoes and four laser cannons provide impressive firepower for a ship of this size.

BORROWED SPEED

Jedi missions are unpredictable and you can't always expect the perfect vehicle to be ready and waiting. Sometimes you have to improvise with what's available.

TATOOINE SWOOP BIKE

Anakin borrows Owen Lars's swoop bike for his search for his mother. This utilitarian, repulsorlift bike is perfect for the sand dunes of Tatooine.

HOTH SNOWSPEEDER

On the icy planet of Hoth, Luke flies a T-47 snowspeeder. These agile two-seaters are civilian craft that have been adapted for battle with dual forward-facing cannons and a rear harpoon gun.

CORUSCANT AIRSPEEDER

Anakin's choice for a high-speed chase was a good one. This open-cockpit, twin turbojet-engine luxury speeder zips through the busy traffic over Coruscant.

Anakin refuses to abandon his Master. He shunts his ship into Obi-Wan's in the hope of knocking the buzz droids off. They are all dislodged apart from one—which crawls onto Anakin's ship!

WHAT DO YOU DO WHEN BUZZ DROIDS ATTACK?

BUZZ DROIDS ARE BAD NEWS for a pilot. These small, scuttling robots cling to a ship and dismantle it from the outside in. Above Coruscant, Obi-Wan's ETA-2 Interceptor is attacked by buzz droids, which start shutting down its systems. Firing at them is no good, because it risks destroying the ship! The only way to defeat them is teamwork.

Astromech droids are perfectly positioned on the outside of ships to target buzz droids. However, Obi-Wan's astromech droid, R4-P17, is no match for them and he is pulled apart in seconds. Anakin's droid, R2-D2, is made of sterner stuff. He zaps the buzz droid right in its center eye.

Kit **FISTO**

SENSORY HEAD TENTACLES

Kit Fisto is a popular Jedi Master, respected as much for his fighting skill as for his ready smile. An easygoing Jedi, Kit values friendship as highly as he values the Jedi Code.

UNBLINKING, BIG EYES GIVE EXCELLENT NIGHT VISION

SENSITIVE

Kit is able to breathe in both air and water. He also has tentacles sprouting from his head, which he uses to sense the feelings of those around him. Being able to detect changing emotions enhances Kit's people skills, and gives him an edge on the battlefield.

LIGHTSABER ADAPTED TO BE WATERPROOF

BRAVE TO THE END

Kit Fisto is not one to stand still when villains are nearby. He joins Mace Windu on his mission to arrest Chancellor Palpatine, but is killed when Palpatine draws his lightsaber and attacks.

JEDI STATS

SPECIES: NAUTOLAN

HOMEWORLD: GLEE ANSELM

BIRTHDATE: UNKNOWN

HEIGHT: 1.96 M (6 FT 5 IN)

RANK: JEDI MASTER

TRAINED BY: UNKNOWN

PREFERRED COMBAT STYLE: FORM I (SHII-CHO)

TRADEMARK: FRIENDLINESS

Plo **KOON**

JEDI STATS

SPECIES: KEL DOR
HOMEWORLD: DORIN
BIRTHDATE: UNKNOWN
HEIGHT: 1.88 M (6 FT 2 IN)
RANK: JEDI MASTER
TRAINED BY: UNKNOWN
PREFERRED COMBAT STYLE: FORM V (DJEM SO/SHIEN)
TRADEMARK: DECISIVENESS

Plo Koon is a senior member of the Jedi Council. This stern Jedi Master is known for making fast decisions. Plo's ability to act quickly makes him both a fierce warrior and a fearsome starship pilot.

THICK KEL DOR HIDE

GAS MASK FOR OXYGEN-RICH ATMOSPHERES

STARFIGHTER HERO

As a Jedi General, Plo was one of the best pilots in the Republic Fleet. The mere sight of his blade-shaped starfighter terrified his enemies. But when his own troops opened fire on his ship during Order 66, Plo could do nothing to save himself.

MAN OF CONVICTION

Plo is motivated by a strict sense of right and wrong. Although he is always focused on hunting down the bad guys, he displays such concern for his troops that he has been known to risk his own life to save theirs.

TOOLS OF THE TRADE

THE JEDI TEMPLE is full of useful gadgets. Whether you are training a new Padawan, searching for an underwater city, taking on an AT-AT walker, or traveling to the Outer Rim, make sure you take along the right tools. You never know when they'll come in handy.

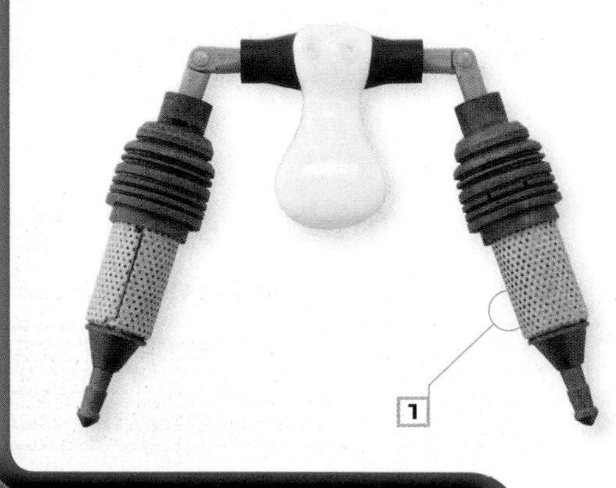

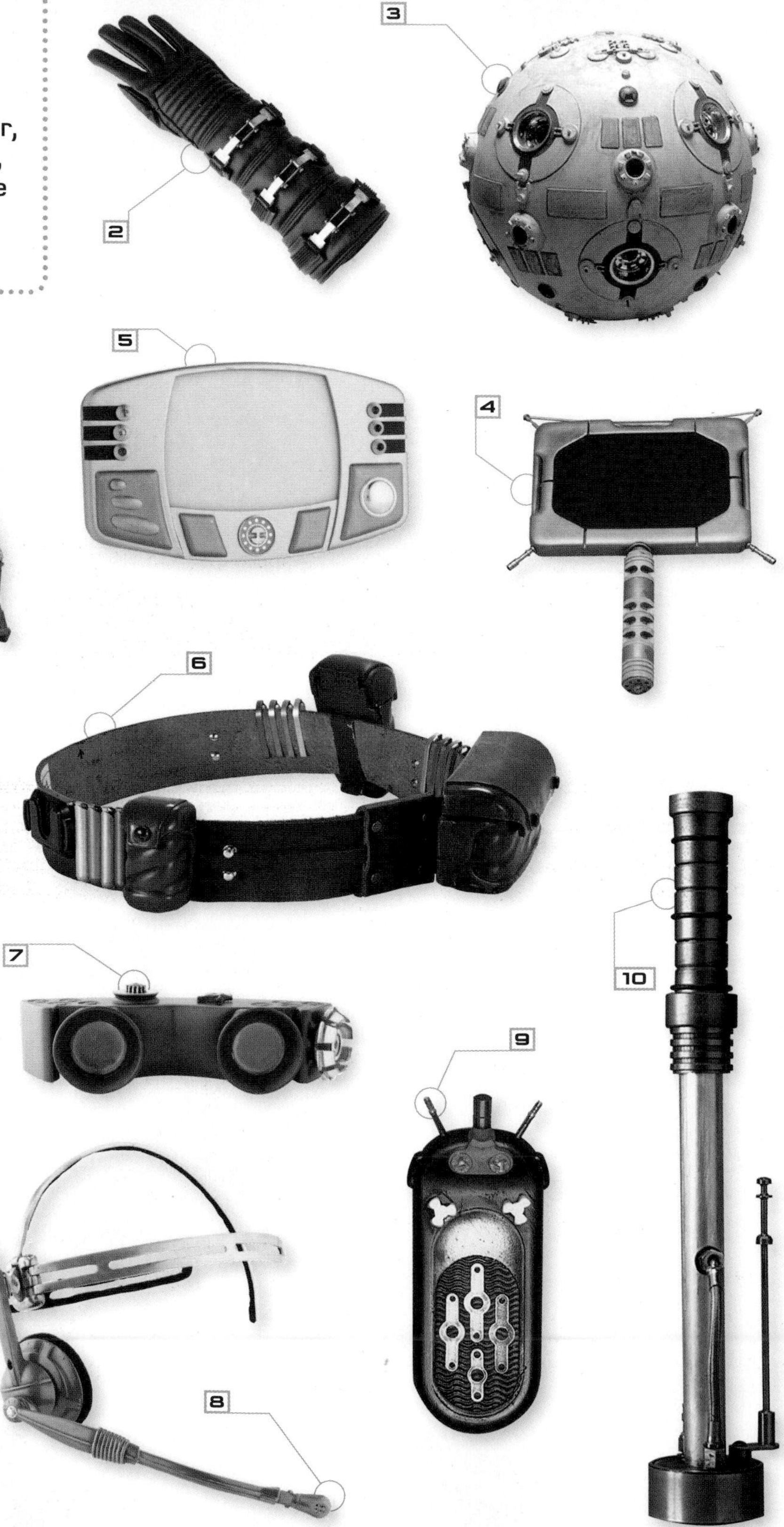

KEY

1. A99 AQUATA BREATHER to enable breathing underwater, in outer space, or in a poisonous environment.

2. Auto-seal, close fitting GLOVE to cover and protect artificial limbs.

3. TRAINING REMOTE to fire harmless beams at Padawans during lightsaber training.

4. Force-operated TESTING SCREEN to constantly challenge Padawans.

5. VIEWSCREEN to view incoming communications.

6. UTILITY BELT with storage pouches and food capsules.

7. MACROBINOCULARS for extreme long distance and outer space viewing.

8. HEADSET COMLINK to enable communication when in flight.

9. Security-enhanced COMLINK to send and receive audio messages.

10. CABLE RETRIEVER to retrieve grappling hook line.

11. TRACER BEACON to track a moving target.

12. SCANNER MONITOR to detect nearby movement, life-forms, metal, or communication signals.

13. BINOCULARS to observe long distances.

14. IMAGE ENHANCER for when transmissions are coming from exceptionally long distances.

15. HOVER CHAIR to enable easier transport within Jedi Temple.

16. TRAINING LIGHTSABER for Younglings with reduced-size hilt and low-energy blade.

17. LIGHTSABER for use during battles and duels.

18. HOLOPROJECTOR to send and receive secure, encrypted holotransmissions.

19. GRAPPLING HOOK for leaping extremely high or crossing large chasms.

20. Sturdy UTILITY POUCH with built-in grappling hook and line.

HOW CAN YOU DESTROY A DEATH STAR?

All the brave Y-wing pilots of Gold Squadron, except one, are destroyed by Imperial fire. Next, Red Squadron gets to work in their X-wings, but the mission is just too hard. Pilot after pilot is defeated, until only one remains.

The last hope lies with Luke Skywalker. But he is no ordinary pilot: The Force is strong with him. To the horror of the other Rebels, Luke switches off his tracking computer. He hears Obi-Wan telling him that if he trusts in the Force and listens to his feelings, then the Force will guide him.

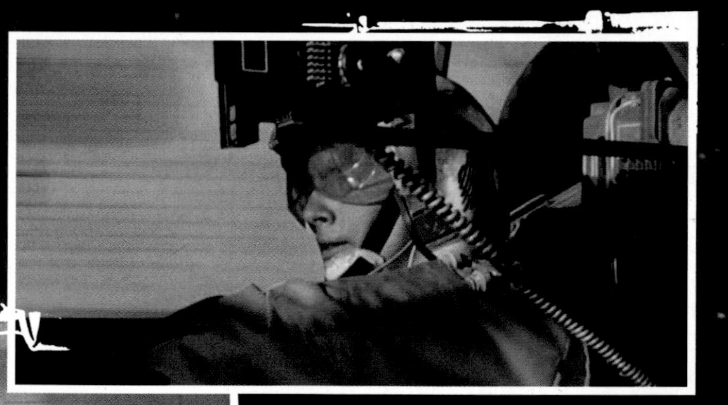

Bullseye! Luke launches the proton torpedo right on target. It begins a chain reaction that causes the whole station to explode. There's just enough time for Luke to get out of there before he is engulfed in flames.

THE GIANT ARMORED station called the Death Star is like the Empire that created it—huge, powerful, and dangerous. It seems impossible to defeat, but the resourceful Rebel Alliance has found its weakness: One direct hit on a small exhaust port opening will reduce the monster to rubble. Getting close to it, however, is no easy task.

JEDI COMRADES

The Jedi Order is made up of beings from every corner of the galaxy. Species, age, height, or gender are not important; it matters only that you are attuned to the Force and committed to the Jedi way. Every Jedi has something unique to offer the Order.

STRONG WILLED

SPECIES: THOLOTHIAN
HOMEWORLD: THOLOTH

STASS ALLIE seeks peace, but she believes that sometimes you have to fight in order to achieve it.

FALLEN JEDI

SPECIES: CHALACTAN
HOMEWORLD: CORUSCANT

DEPA BILLABA sees terrible things in the Clone Wars and her troubled emotions lead her to the dark side.

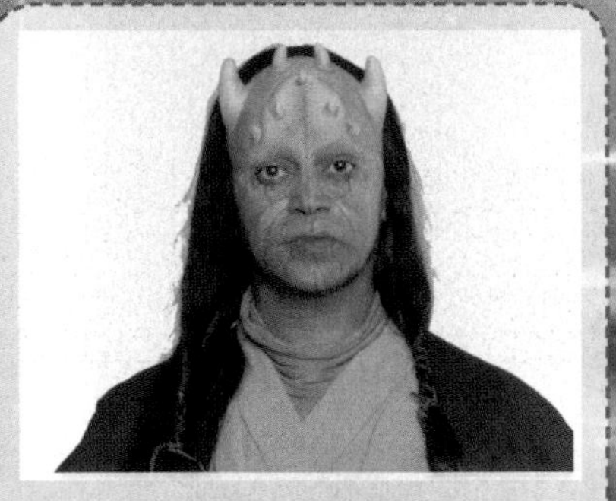

WILL OF STEEL

SPECIES: IRIDONIAN ZABRAK
HOMEWORLD: NAR SHADDAA

EETH KOTH works so hard at disciplining his mind that he can withstand great physical pain.

SUPER-SENSORY

SPECIES: TOGRUTA
HOMEWORLD: SHILI

SHAAK TI's hollow headtails allow her to sense her surroundings ultrasonically or duck blaster fire.

WAR WISDOM

SPECIES: THISSPIASIAN
HOMEWORLD: THISSPIAS

OPPO RANCISIS is a military mastermind and the Republic's secret weapon in the Clone Wars.

ATHLETIC JEDI

SPECIES: HUMAN
HOMEWORLD: KUAT

BULTAR SWAN is a fan of martial arts and this greatly influences the way she swings her lightsaber.

POWERFUL JEDI

SPECIES: UNKNOWN
HOMEWORLD: UNKNOWN

YADDLE has mastered Morichro—the ability to control others' body functions such as their breathing.

INJURED JEDI

SPECIES: LANNIK
HOMEWORLD: LANNIK

EVEN PIELL lost an eye in battle and he wears his scars as a reminder of past troubles.

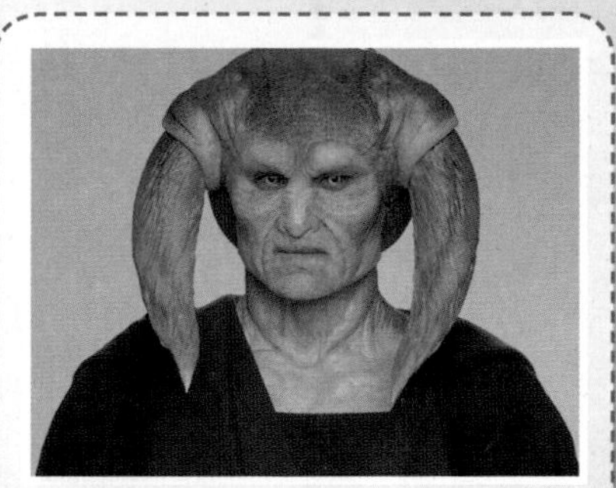

LONER

SPECIES: IKTOTCHI
HOMEWORLD: IKTOTCH

SAESEE TIIN likes to spend time alone, meditating and honing his skill of foresight.

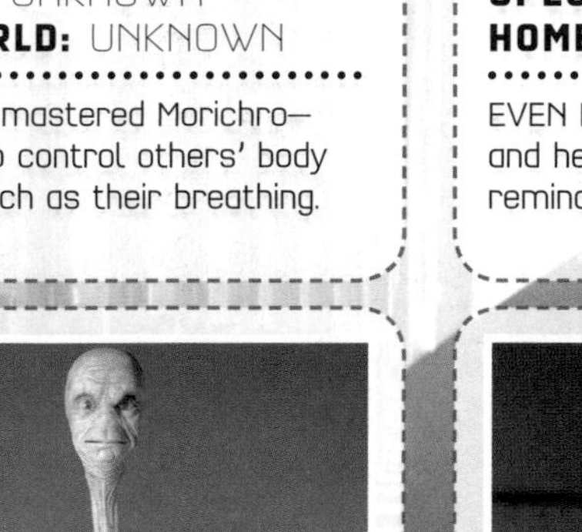

CUNNING JEDI

SPECIES: QUERMIAN
HOMEWORLD: QUERMIA

YARAEL POOF prefers not to use weapons—he uses his mastery of mind trickery against his enemies.

FAITHFUL JEDI

SPECIES: THOLOTHIAN
HOMEWORLD: CORUSCANT

ADI GALLIA is Stass Allie's cousin. She was inspired to be a Jedi as a child, when Even Piell saved her life.

FIERCE FIGHTER

SPECIES: IRIDONIAN ZABRAK
HOMEWORLD: CORUSCANT

AGEN KOLAR is no diplomat. Instead he prefers to influence people in battle, with his lightsaber.

OPEN-MINDED

SPECIES: ONGREE
HOMEWORLD: SKUSTELL

COLEMAN KCAJ's face shape allows him to see different angles. He can also see many sides to a problem.

LANGUAGE MASTER

SPECIES: VURK
HOMEWORLD: SEMBLA

COLEMAN TREBOR is a skilled communicator. He becomes the spokesperson for the Jedi Order.

BOOKWORM

SPECIES: HUMAN
HOMEWORLD: CORUSCANT

JOCASTA NU is a Consular Jedi. She is an academic, not a soldier, and looks after the Jedi Archives.

THE [illegible]AT[illegible] T[illegible] T[illegible]...

DEDICATION
Qui-Gon's dying wish is that Obi-Wan train Anakin. Although he is sometimes hot-headed and impatient, Anakin becomes a loyal Padawan.

ANGER
When his mother dies at the hands of Tusken Raiders, Anakin's anger consumes him. He destroys whole clan.

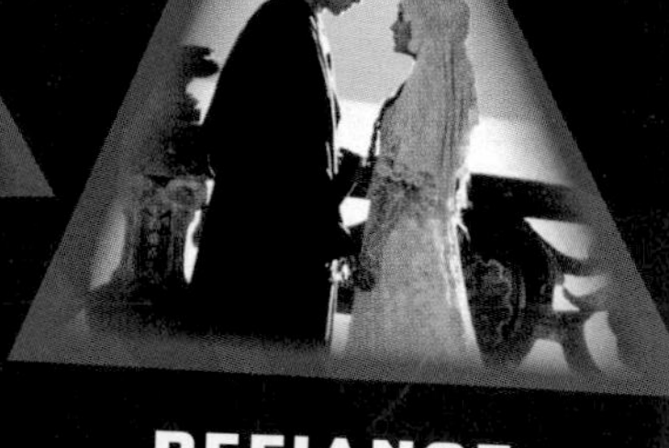

DEFIANCE
Anakin breaks the Jedi Code by marrying Padmé Amidala in secret. His love makes him so afraid of losing her that he is blinded to all else.

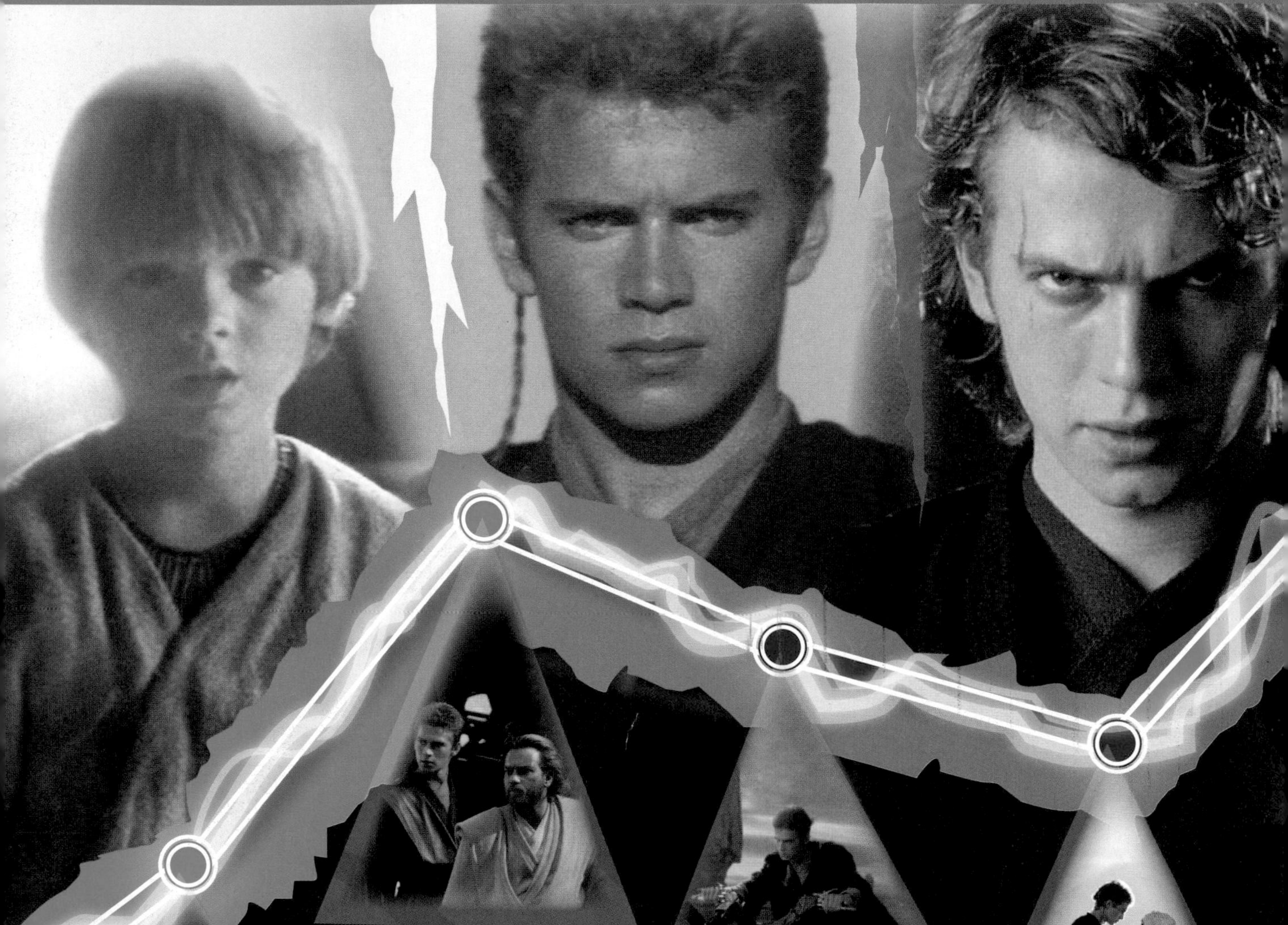

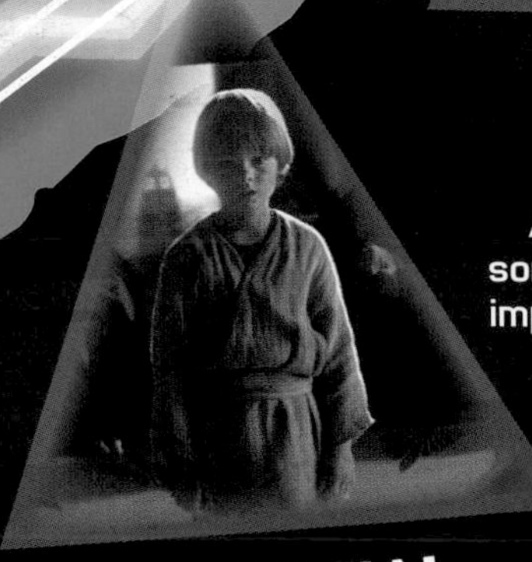

POTENTIAL
As a child, Anakin shows great skill, but also much fear. The Jedi Council is unable to see his future and Anakin is too old, so it refuses to train him.

DARK SIDE

Anakin Skywalker is a great Jedi, but he struggles to control his feelings and greed. If Jedi do not keep their emotions in check, they are open to the temptations of the dark side. Darth Sidious covets Anakin as a Sith Apprentice so he plays with Anakin's emotions until they consume him and draw him over to the dark side.

POWER

During the Clone Wars, Anakin proves himself to be a brave Jedi hero. But he still wants more and feels that the Jedi are holding him back.

HATE

Anakin is goaded by Darth Sidious into killing Count Dooku. It is not the Jedi way to kill an unarmed prisoner, but Anakin gives in to his emotions.

GREED

Anakin is terrified Padmé will die. Darth Sidious claims he can save her, so Anakin greedily chooses the Sith over his fellow Jedi, and Mace dies.

EVIL

Anakin is given the Sith name Darth Vader. After fighting his old Master, Obi-Wan, Vader needs a metal suit to keep him alive. His journey to the dark side is complete.

WHAT HAPPENS WHEN A STUDENT TURNS ON HIS TEACHER?

THE BOND BETWEEN MASTER and Padawan is strong. From the moment Anakin turns to the dark side, a confrontation with his Master Obi-Wan Kenobi becomes inevitable. On Mustafar, Anakin rejects Obi-Wan's attempts to reason with him. Now serving a new master, a Sith master, Anakin isn't about to let any Jedi get in his way—even if that Jedi is one of his oldest friends.

Anakin and Obi-Wan have fought as a team countless times. They know each others' best moves—and weaknesses. Now transformed from friends to foes, they seem evenly matched. But Anakin overestimates his own skills, and his arrogance is his downfall.

DARTH TYRANUS

Long ago Count Dooku rejected the Order that trained him as a Jedi. When Darth Maul is killed, Dooku becomes Darth Sidious's new Apprentice, Darth Tyranus.

DARTH MAUL

A Dathomirian trained in secret by Darth Sidious, Darth Maul is the first Sith to reveal himself for 1,000 years.

BEWARE THE SITH

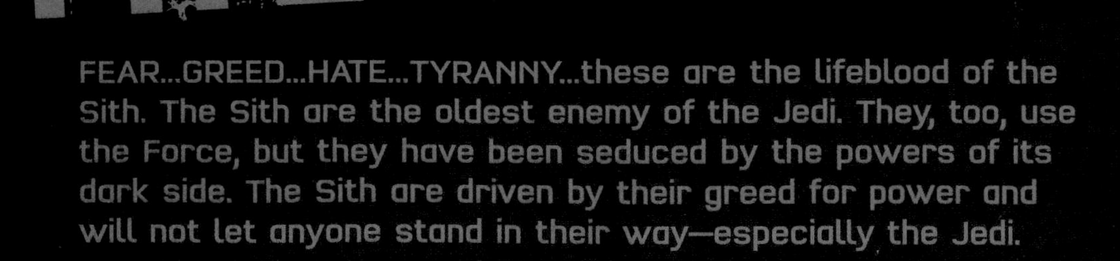

FEAR...GREED...HATE...TYRANNY...these are the lifeblood of the Sith. The Sith are the oldest enemy of the Jedi. They, too, use the Force, but they have been seduced by the powers of its dark side. The Sith are driven by their greed for power and will not let anyone stand in their way—especially the Jedi.

DARTH VADER

Darth Vader is Sidious's final Apprentice. Vader is controlled by his Master and no longer bears any resemblance to the man he once was—Anakin Skywalker. His body is so damaged that he is dependent on a metal suit to keep him alive.

DARTH SIDIOUS

The Dark Lord of the Sith, Darth Sidious is a master of deception. For decades he fools everyone into thinking that he is the kind and peaceful Palpatine. In this guise, he rises to the position of Supreme Chancellor of the Republic and manipulates both sides in the Clone Wars. When the time comes to fulfill his master plan, he destroys the Republic and installs himself as Emperor of a new galactic order.

JEDI WISDOM

■ The Rule of Two states that there can be only two Sith at a time: one Master and one Apprentice. When Darth Sidious wants Anakin as an Apprentice, he manipulates him into killing Darth Tyranus.

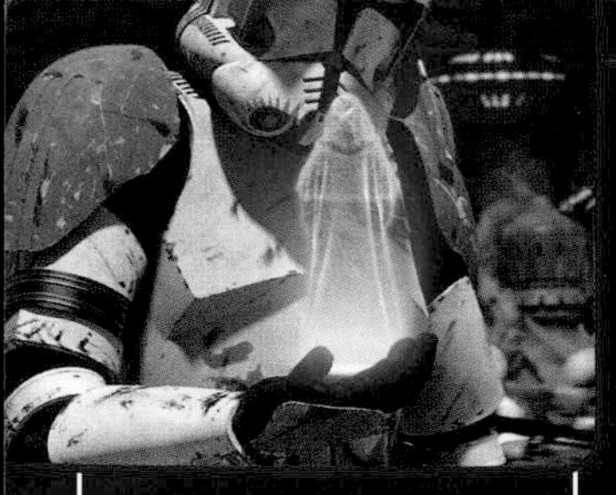

BREAKING NEWS: Rumors circulate that the clone troopers of the Republic Army have received executive orders from Chancellor Palpatine...

ORDER 66 IS a secret military instruction created by Chancellor Palpatine to help him take over the galaxy. The Clone Army is programmed to follow the orders of the Chancellor, so when he gives Order 66, they have to act. The Clone Army turn on their former allies, the Jedi, with deadly consequences...

...UTAPAU: Commander Cody orders an AT-TE clone pilot to fire on Obi-Wan Kenobi...Jedi believed to have escaped...order issued to shoot on sight...

...FELUCIA: Commander Bly and the 327th Star Corps turn on Aayla Secura...Jedi confirmed dead...

...SALEUCAMI: Commander Neyo and CT-3423 fire on Stass Allie...death confirmed...

...MYGEETO: Galactic Marines led by Commander Bacara attack and kill Ki-Adi-Mundi...mission complete...

...CATO NEIMOIDIA: Plo Koon's Delta-7 starfighter shot down by Captain Jag...wreckage confirms pilot dead...

...KASHYYYK: 41st Elite Corps trooper and Commander Gree sneak up on Yoda...soldiers killed in counterattack... suspect fled...order issued to shoot on sight...

...CORUSCANT: Anakin Skywalker now loyal to Sith...leads 501st clone trooper legion in raid on Jedi Temple...no survivors...

...THE DARK TIMES BEGIN...

WHAT HAPPENS WHEN OLD ENEMIES MEET?

JEDI WISDOM

■ Some Jedi, like Obi-Wan, can make themselves one with the Force. This means that they can live on after death as part of the Force.

TWENTY YEARS HAVE passed since Darth Vader and Obi-Wan dueled on Mustafar. Aboard the Death Star, the former Jedi Master and his Padawan meet again. There is only hatred and revenge on Vader's mind, but Obi-Wan is serving a more important purpose. While the Rebels attempt to rescue Princess Leia, Obi-Wan engages Vader in a duel.

Although Obi-Wan is still a match for Darth Vader, he allows himself to be killed in the duel, giving Luke and the Rebels precious time to escape. Unlike Vader, who tries to control death, Obi-Wan is willing to submit to it: He passes over to the non-physical to show Luke that his spirit can continue beyond death.

SEPARATED AT BIRTH
When Luke sets off to rescue a princess, he finds more than he bargained for: a twin sister. He is fiercely protective of his sister, Leia, and does everything he can to keep her safe.

Luke always sees the good in people, even someone as cruel as Darth Vader. He never gives up hope that his father will change.

Luke SKYWALKER

Luke is an adventure-seeking boy from Tatooine who brings new hope to the Rebel Alliance and the few remaining Jedi. He comes to Jedi training late in life, but the Force is strong with him and he is guided by a wiser Obi-Wan and Yoda. Luke faces a daunting task: to defeat Darth Vader and the Emperor.

JEDI STATS

SPECIES: HUMAN
HOMEWORLD: BORN ON POLIS MASSA; RAISED ON TATOOINE
BIRTHDATE: 19 BBY
HEIGHT: 1.72 M (5 FT 8 IN)
RANK: JEDI MASTER
TRAINED BY: OBI-WAN & YODA
WEAPON: BLUE & LATER A GREEN-BLADED LIGHTSABER
PREFERRED COMBAT STYLE: FORM V (SHIEN/DJEM SO)
TRADEMARK: LOYALTY

EXCEPTIONAL CONNECTION WITH THE FORCE

HIS FATHER'S SON?

Luke's father is Anakin Skywalker. Like him, Luke is a good pilot and has a knack for knowing how to fix things, and he can also be impatient and reckless. However, Luke differs from his father in one key way: Despite the Emperor's best efforts, Luke refuses to submit to the dark side.

LIGHTSABER ONCE BELONGED TO ANAKIN

FAITHFUL FRIEND

Luke shows great loyalty to his friends, even the droids. To Luke, astromech droid R2-D2 is far more than just a robot, and he wouldn't swap him for the world.

Wampas are deadly ice creatures who aren't fussy about what or whom they eat. A human wouldn't normally stand a chance against these mighty beasts, but Luke has a special weapon—the Force.

HOW CAN YOU ESCAPE FROM A FIERCE WAMPA?

Luke closes his eyes and concentrates hard—just like Obi-Wan taught him. After a few moments, the lightsaber zips through the air, right into Luke's hand! He uses it to cut himself down and escape the wampa.

PATROLLING THE FREEZING plains of Hoth, Luke Skywalker is attacked by a wampa ice monster. The next thing he knows, he's suspended by his ankles in an icy cave. Luke knows he's in trouble. If only he could reach his lightsaber, lying just a few feet away...

HOW CAN THE LIGHT SIDE OF THE FORCE DEFEAT THE DARK SIDE?

During a gruesome duel on Cloud City, Vader desperately wants Luke to join him on the dark side. He appeals to him as a father and offers Luke the chance to destroy the Emperor once and for all. But Luke's belief in the light side of the Force is so strong, he will not be turned, even when facing death.

Luke resists the dark side again during another duel with his father on the second Death Star. Luke's extreme dedication to the light side shames his father, and when the Emperor attempts to kill Luke, Vader hears Luke's pleas and rescues his son. As he dies, Vader finally finds peace in the light side of the Force.

THE AGE-OLD battle between Jedi and Sith, between the light and dark sides of the Force, has always hinged on temptation. Sith Lords often recruit Jedi with promises of incredible power. However, sometimes the desire for honor and justice can be powerful too.

“THE DARK SIDE OF THE
IS A PATHWAY
ABILITIES...

...SOME
CONSIDER
TO BE
UNNATURAL."

Throughout history, the struggle between darkness and light has shaped the galaxy. Both the Sith and the Jedi study the mystical energy known as the Force. The Sith lust for power, and use the dark side of the Force to destroy their enemies, while the Jedi turn to the light side in their quest for peace and justice. The Sith despise the noble ideals of the Jedi, and will not rest until the Jedi Order is destroyed.

The Jedi Order was created by Force-sensitive beings who study the light side of the Force. Their honorable quest for galactic peace, however, is often undermined by the existence of the Sith and their dark motives. When the Sith reemerge after millennia of silence, the Jedi Order has no choice: it is time for war.

ANCIENT

The Sith Order was founded by a group of wayward Jedi. Dissatisfied with the teachings of the light side, these former Jedi Knights turned to the dark side in search of greater power. The Sith have concealed their presence from the Jedi for over 1,000 years, waiting for the perfect time to make their return.

HATRED

THE DARK SIDE

Fear and mystery surround the dark side of the Force. Whispered stories and strange rumours are all that is known about the Sith and their deadly powers. The Sith rule from the shadows, using their terrible powers to shroud the galaxy in darkness and bend others to their will. There is only one way to discover all the secrets of the dark side—by joining the Sith.

TERRIFYING POWER

RUTHLESS AMBITION

SECRET TEACHINGS

UNSPEAKABLE EVIL

THE SITH CODE

Peace is a lie, there is only passion.
Through passion, I gain strength.
Through strength, I gain power.
Through power, I gain victory.
Through victory, my chains are broken.
The Force shall free me.

The Rule OF TWO

In the past, there were many Sith. They studied the Force and grew powerful—but they also became suspicious of each other. Fighting broke out among them and the Sith Order was greatly weakened. The Rule of Two was introduced to prevent the power of the dark side from destroying the Order.

POWER HUNGRY

The Rule of Two states that there can be only one Sith Master and only one apprentice at any time. When the apprentice grows more powerful than his Master, he is to destroy him and choose an apprentice of his own. But the Rule of Two has a flaw: the Sith Code encourages passion and ambition—not loyalty. As long as the Sith exist, there will always be a brutal struggle for power.

SITH SECRETS

■ Darth Bane was a Sith Lord who lived over 1,000 years ago. He became dissatisfied with his Sith brotherhood and created his own Sith Order, in which he instituted the Rule of Two.

APPRENTICE'S APPRENTICE

Many Sith apprentices don't obey the Rule of Two and secretly take on their own apprentices. Sidious began training Darth Maul before he had destroyed his own Master, Darth Plagueis. Darth Tyranus trained Asajj Ventress and Savage Opress while he was Sidious's apprentice, and Darth Vader had a secret apprentice named Galen Marek.

EXPENDABLE APPRENTICE

Darth Tyranus is Sidious's second apprentice, but he is needed only until Sidious succeeds in turning Anakin Skywalker to the dark side. Sidious does not expect Tyranus's powers to eclipse his own, and plans to have Tyranus destroyed when the time is right.

UNWANTED APPRENTICE

Darth Sidious watched Anakin for years before the Jedi became his Sith apprentice. But Darth Vader was gravely wounded by Obi-Wan on the volcano planet Mustafar, so he now feels trapped in his armored body. Vader is no longer the apprentice that Sidious hoped he would be.

"TWO THERE SHOULD BE. NO MORE, NO LESS. ONE TO EMBODY POWER, THE OTHER TO CRAVE IT."

DARTH BANE

SITH SELECTION

Are your Force powers exceptional? Do you care only about yourself? Is it hard to control your feelings of anger and greed? Do you think you should be more powerful than anyone else? These are some of the dark qualities Darth Sidious searches for in a new Sith apprentice.

DARTH MAUL

Raw power • Aggressive • Obedient

STRONG-MINDEDNESS: 5
LIGHTSABER SKILL: 7
FORCE SKILL: 8
RAW POWER: 9
CUNNING: 3

Darth Maul has been honing his dark side skills since he was a child. He is a talented, agile fighter and will obey his Master without question. Maul is naturally strong in the Force, but is he too confident?

DARTH TYRANUS

Ambitious • Intelligent • Remorseless

STRONG-MINDEDNESS: 7
LIGHTSABER SKILL: 10
FORCE SKILL: 7
RAW POWER: 6
CUNNING: 8

Former Jedi Count Dooku is arrogant and ambitious. His never-ending search for power means he will be unable to resist the temptation of the dark side. Darth Tyranus is immensely powerful, but can he defeat his former Jedi allies?

A NEW APPRENTICE

Choosing a Sith apprentice is an important decision. Darth Sidious considers the personality, skills, and raw power of his candidates so he can choose wisely. Then he exploits their weaknesses and promises them what they desire in an effort to lure them to the dark side.

DARTH VADER

Emotional • Impatient • Open to temptation

STRONG-MINDEDNESS:	8
LIGHTSABER SKILL:	9
FORCE SKILL:	9
RAW POWER:	8
CUNNING:	5

Jedi Anakin Skywalker conceals a growing frustration with the Jedi Code. His troubled memories, feelings of fear, and emotional greed make him a perfect Sith candidate. Blinded by his own feelings, will Anakin succumb to the dark side?

LUKE SKYWALKER

Strong in the Force • Impulsive • Naive

STRONG-MINDEDNESS:	10
LIGHTSABER SKILL:	8
FORCE SKILL:	9
RAW POWER:	7
CUNNING:	6

Luke Skywalker is eager to learn the truth about his father, Anakin. Luke's innocence might lead him to underestimate the power of the dark side. Is he strong-minded enough to resist?

A SMILING VILLAIN
Posing as Chancellor Palpatine, Darth Sidious conceals his Sith identity for years, waiting for the right time to reveal himself. He uses his alter ego to influence the decisions of the Republic, discover the workings of the Jedi Order, and seek out a new, powerful Sith apprentice.

As Emperor, Darth Sidious is in control of the entire galaxy. His appearance suggests an old, frail man—but don't be fooled! Sidious possesses almost unlimited Force powers.

Darth SIDIOUS

It has been many centuries since a Sith Lord was powerful enough to step out from the shadows. Darth Sidious spent years gathering his strength, destroying his enemies, and watching his deadly plans play out. Now, as Emperor Palpatine, he has emerged from hiding and placed the galaxy under Sith control.

SITH STATS

SPECIES: HUMAN

HOMEWORLD: NABOO

BIRTHDATE: 82 BBY

HEIGHT: 5 FT 8 IN (1.73 M)

TRAINED BY: DARTH PLAGUEIS

WEAPONS: RED-BLADED LIGHTSABER

TRADEMARK: SITH LIGHTNING

BLACK ZEYD-CLOTH ROBES GIVE SIDIOUS AN AIR OF SECRECY

HIDDEN THREAT

Darth Sidious will do whatever it takes to get what he wants: he uses his immense dark side powers to manipulate, betray, and murder. Sidious also uses secrecy as a weapon, concealing his face under his dark cloak to hide his true identity.

TWO MASTERS

The dark and light sides of the Force clash when Darth Sidious duels Yoda in the Senate building. Sidious battles with passion and fury, only to be matched at every blow by Yoda's calm, measured skill. Although unable to defeat Yoda, Sidious's strength forces the Jedi to flee.

SITH PLAN:
TAKE CONTROL

Darth Sidious's alter ego Palpatine is the respected Senator of Naboo. The Sith Lord has evil plans in store for the galaxy, but he requires a lot more political power to carry them out. Sidious devises a cunning five-step strategy, designed to turn a simple Senator into an all-powerful leader. So begins his rise to power...

1. CREATE A PROBLEM

OBJECTIVE:
Create unrest in the Senate by initiating a political disturbance.

OUTCOME:
Invasion of Naboo and resulting conflict sparks fear and uncertainty in the Senate.
MISSION COMPLETE.

2. BECOME SUPREME CHANCELLOR

OBJECTIVE:
Cause the Senate to lose confidence in the current Chancellor, Valorum.

OUTCOME:
Manipulated by Palpatine, Queen Amidala calls for new Senate election. Palpatine is voted Supreme Chancellor.
MISSION COMPLETE.

"Hundreds of Senators are now UNDER THE INFLUENCE of a Sith Lord."

COUNT DOOKU

3. ESTABLISH TRUST

OBJECTIVE:
Palpatine to gain the trust and support of the Senate and Jedi Order.

OUTCOME:
Palpatine is included and applauded in the Naboo celebrations.
MISSION COMPLETE.

4. GAIN EMERGENCY POWERS

OBJECTIVE:
Palpatine to increase his powers and gain more control over Senate.

OUTCOME:
Jar Jar Binks proposes the Senate gives emergency powers to Palpatine.
MISSION COMPLETE.

5. JEDI COUNCIL SPY

OBJECTIVE:
Palpatine to place a spy on the Jedi Council.

OUTCOME:
Anakin Skywalker appointed as Jedi Council member.
MISSION COMPLETE.

CONSEQUENCES:

Darth Sidious is now in a prime position to be kept informed of all the happenings of the Republic. As Supreme Chancellor Palpatine, he has more power than ever before and he is able to control the actions of the Galactic Senate. But Sidious hasn't finished: he will not stop until he destroys the Jedi Order.

OFFICE OF THE CHANCELLOR

When Chancellor Palpatine discusses political matters in his office in the Senate building, no one suspects his true Sith identity. But the devious Palpatine cannot resist designing his office to hint at a darker personality. If you look closely, you'll find a surprising number of references to the Sith among the Chancellor's possessions.

CEREMONIAL OFFICE

ARMORED CHAIR

The Chancellor's grand and airy Ceremonial Office is used for official meetings. Palpatine's Chair of Office looks ordinary, but it is built from lanthanide armor and is protected by a state-of-the-art defense shield. The arms feature a built-in comlink to summon the Red Guard.

DARK ORNAMENT

Those who have studied the teachings of the dark side will recognize this Sith Chalice. It houses sacred Korribanian incense for conducting a Sith Fire Ritual. Palpatine displays it in plain sight, confident that no one will realize its true origins.

RELICS OF THE SITH

Two ornate black vases stand by the entrance to the Private Office. Visitors never enter this room, so Palpatine has not tried to mask his sinister taste. These objects are Spirit Urns, which hold the remains of former Sith Lords, including Sidious's Master, Darth Plagueis.

KEEPING SECRETS

The Chancellor's Private Office is perfect for top-secret meetings. Palpatine uses the computer equipment in this room to communicate with his Sith apprentice and to store his plans for the Death Star project.

PRIVATE OFFICE

HIDDEN WEAPON

Four statues in the office show the Sages of Dwartii, ancient, controversial philosophers. The statue of Sistros stands just outside the Private Office, and it has a special purpose: it conceals Palpatine's lightsaber in a chamber behind its arms.

DECEPTIVE ART

An enormous, sculpted artwork hangs in an antechamber between the Ceremonial and Private Office. It depicts a battle between Jedi and Sith during the Great Hyperspace War of 5,000 BBY. Although the Jedi were victorious, if you look closely, the artwork glorifies the Sith warriors.

Sith LIGHTSABERS

The Sith possess enough Force power to battle without a lightsaber, but each new apprentice chooses his own weapon as part of his training. Sith lightsabers are powered by synthetic red crystals, which emit a strong crimson blade—reflecting the Sith's passion, bloodlust, and rage.

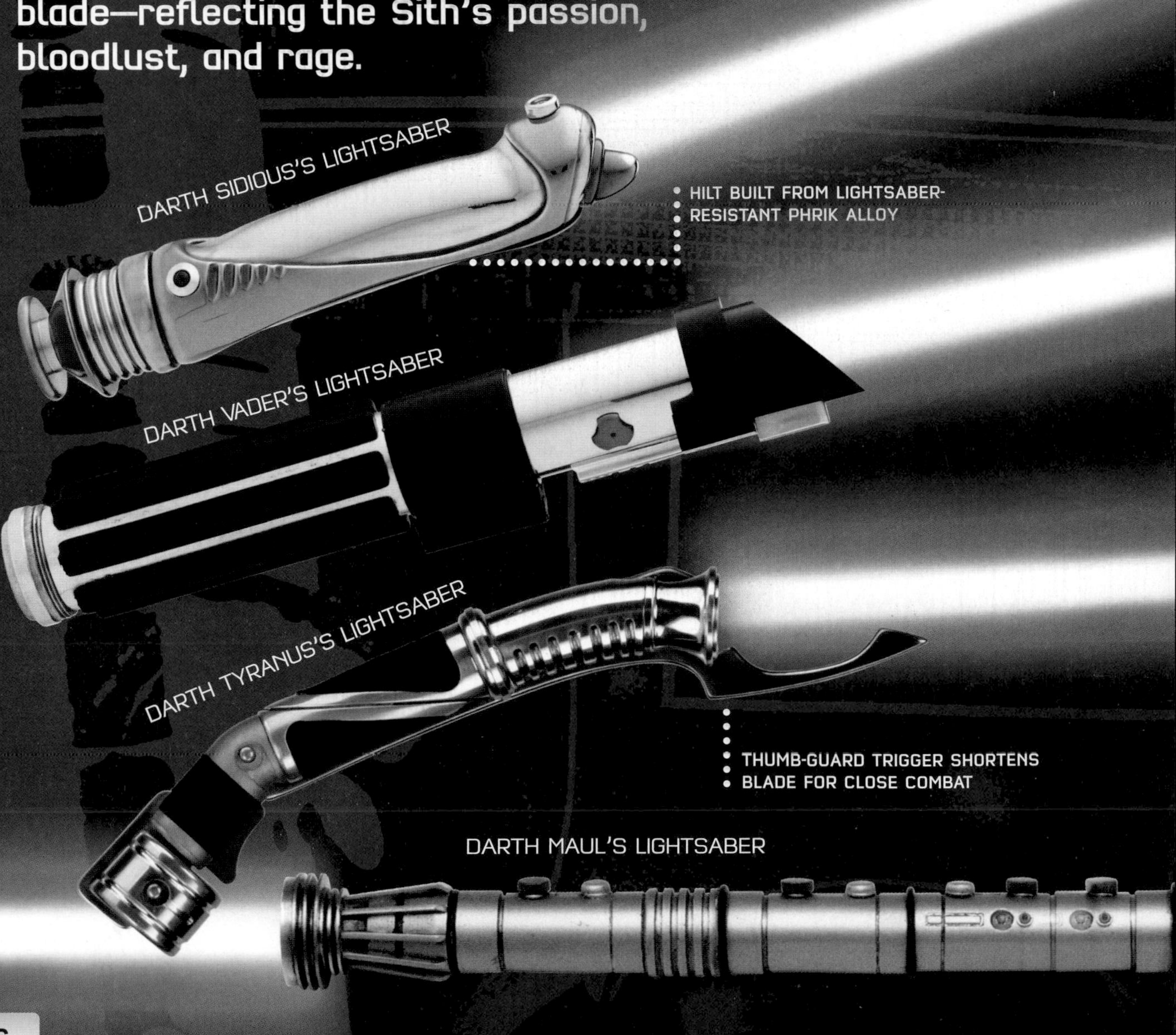

DARTH SIDIOUS'S LIGHTSABER

HILT BUILT FROM LIGHTSABER-RESISTANT PHRIK ALLOY

DARTH VADER'S LIGHTSABER

DARTH TYRANUS'S LIGHTSABER

THUMB-GUARD TRIGGER SHORTENS BLADE FOR CLOSE COMBAT

DARTH MAUL'S LIGHTSABER

Darth Sidious's ornate aurodium-plated lightsaber hilt reflects his passion for dark objects of antiquity. Its rounded form allows for fluid movement in combat.

Darth Vader's black-alloy lightsaber closely resembles the style of his Jedi weapon. To fit his mechanical hands, however, Vader's lightsaber hilt is larger than normal.

Darth Tyranus uses the same lightsaber he built when he was a Jedi. Its curved hilt is designed for precise handling. When Tyranus became a Sith, Sidious gave him a new red crystal to replace his green blade.

Darth Maul finds a single-bladed lightsaber limiting in combat. His saberstaff is perfect for attacking two opponents at once, but its size means that Maul has to be more acrobatic in battle.

OSTENTATIOUS HAT LOOKS IMPORTANT

TRADE FEDERATION SENATOR

The Trade Federation is so influential, it has its own Senate representative, Lott Dod. Dod is power-hungry and insincere.

TRADE FEDERATION

LEADER: NUTE GUNRAY

ALLEGIANCE: SEPARATISTS

HEADQUARTERS: TRADE FEDERATION BATTLESHIP

WEAPONS: DROID ARMY

VALUES: MONEY, POWER

LOTT DOD

ELABORATE ROBE BOUGHT WITH TRADE FEDERATION CREDITS

NUTE GUNRAY

COWARDLY VICEROY

The Trade Federation Viceroy, Nute Gunray, initially accepted Sith control to gain wealth and power. He revels in his new-found power, but lives in fear of Darth Sidious.

When the Neimoidians realize the extent of Sith power, they regret that they ever made a bargain with the Sith. But it is too late.

A SECRET ARMY

Following Darth Sidious's orders, the Trade Federation secretly creates a heavily armed Droid Army. They deploy the army on the planet Naboo, sparking a galactic crisis.

Pawns of the SITH

The Trade Federation is a powerful organization that governs trade throughout the galaxy. It has, however, become corrupt and greedy. Its Neimoidian leaders conceal their allegiance to the Sith by pretending to carry out political missions.

SITH POWERS

As a member of the Order of the Sith, you will learn to harness the power of the dark side. These powers are deadly and unpredictable—but when used correctly, they are almost unstoppable. If you are cornered by a Jedi Knight, or come face to face with a threatening bounty hunter, call on the dark side of the Force. But remember: using these powers can be extremely dangerous.

FORCE CLOUDING

CHANNEL THROUGH: Mind
SITH EXPERT: Darth Sidious can cloud the Force so completely that the Jedi remain unaware of his Sith identity.
DANGER LEVEL: Low – unless discovered!

MIND CONTROL

CHANNEL THROUGH: Mind
SITH EXPERT: Darth Tyranus can control the minds of most of his enemies—although some Jedi are able to resist.
DANGER LEVEL: Moderate

FORCE CHOKE

CHANNEL THROUGH: Hands
SITH EXPERT: Darth Vader can use the Force to strangle his victims without touching them.
DANGER LEVEL: Moderate

POWER OVER DEATH

CHANNEL THROUGH: Body and mind
SITH EXPERT: Darth Sidious uses his dark side powers to extend his life and to save Anakin from certain death.
DANGER LEVEL: High

SITH LIGHTNING

CHANNEL THROUGH: Hands
SITH EXPERT: Darth Sidious can emit intense bolts of deadly lightning for extended periods of time.
DANGER LEVEL: High

CHANNEL THROUGH: Hands and arms
SITH EXPERT: Darth Tyranus can move extremely heavy objects with very little effort.
DANGER LEVEL: Moderate

FORBIDDEN KNOWLEDGE

CHANNEL THROUGH: Mind
SITH EXPERT: Darth Sidious claims to know the dangerous secret of immortality
DANGER LEVEL: High

WHAT HAPPENS WHEN YOU USE THE POWER OF THE DARK SIDE?

THE DARK SIDE OF the Force offers unlimited power, but harnessing that power requires a terrible sacrifice. The dark side affects its users deeply, damaging their bodies, minds, and souls. And, as Anakin demonstrates when he attacks Padmé on Mustafar, it can even corrupt the most legendary Jedi hero.

UNFORGIVABLE ACTIONS
When Anakin turns to the dark side, his terrible actions corrupt his soul. Under orders to wipe out the Jedi Order, the newly named Darth Vader destroys an entire class of innocent Jedi Younglings.

PHYSICAL TRANSFORMATION

The power of the dark side is so destructive, it can permanently damage a living body. When Darth Sidious fires intense bolts of Sith lightning at Mace Windu, Sidious's eyes turn yellow and his skin wrinkles and sags. Now there is no hiding his Sith identity.

BETRAYAL

Darth Vader uses a Force choke on Padmé until she loses consciousness. He is so consumed by the dark side that he duels with Obi-Wan Kenobi, leaving his wife where she lies.

BECOMING A SITH

If you choose the dark side, you embark on a quest for forbidden knowledge. While you will become incredibly powerful, you will also change. First, you will fall prey to your passion. You will become selfish and greedy. Your family and friends will be afraid of you and grow distant. Eventually, all of these changes will begin to affect your physical body, and it will be transformed by the dark side of the Force.

SENATOR PALPATINE

SUPREME CHANCELLOR

SITH SECRETS

■ To create Sith lightning, a Sith Lord must use a very intense burst of Force power. The great effort it takes to produce this weapon appears to drain Sidious of his energy, permanently transforming his appearance.

THE TRANSFORMATION

If you fully embrace the power of the dark side, your skin will become withered and pale, your eyes will grow bloodshot, and your irises will turn yellow. Darth Sidious maintained his human appearance for many years, but the more he used his powers, the more they affected his body. During his years as Supreme Chancellor, he grew paler and more wrinkled, though he continued to mask his transformation in public. But after using an intense burst of Sith lightning against Mace Windu, Sidious's appearance changed dramatically, forever.

DARTH SIDIOUS

EMPEROR PALPATINE

Ancient **ENEMY**

The Jedi Order has always opposed the Sith: while the Sith revel in darkness, the Jedi seek light. As the Sith plan to start a war, the Jedi strive to keep the peace. And when the Sith attempt to oppress the galaxy, the Jedi Order stands in their way.

Important decisions are made by the Jedi Council. When Anakin Skywalker is brought before them, they are unsure whether he should be trained as a Jedi. The Council detects much fear in the young boy.

WISE LEADER

Master Yoda leads the Jedi in times of peace and war. Renowned for his wisdom, Yoda is usually able to sense Force disturbances, but the Sith can cloud his vision.

COARSE, SIMPLE ROBE IS A SIGN OF HUMILITY

JEDI GENERALS

Sometimes, war is necessary to achieve peace. When the Sith spark the Clone Wars, Jedi Masters, such as Mace Windu and Obi-Wan Kenobi, charge into battle alongside the Clone Army.

OBI-WAN IS FAMOUS FOR KEEPING CALM UNDER PRESSURE

LIGHTSABER POWERED BY UNIQUE VIOLET CRYSTAL

OBI-WAN KENOBI

TROUBLE AT THE TEMPLE

After a thousand years of relative peace, the Jedi are taken by surprise when they are attacked by their own Clone Army. Although the Jedi try to resist, their Temple is destroyed and the survivors are forced into exile.

JEDI ORDER

LEADER: YODA

ALLEGIANCE: REPUBLIC

HEADQUARTERS: CORUSCANT

WEAPONS: LIGHTSABER, CLONE ARMY

VALUES: JUSTICE, PEACE, LOYALTY, HONOR

TOUGH, LEATHER COMBAT BOOTS

SITH ARTIFACTS

The Sith treasure ancient objects that reflect their grand history. Even though they usually live in hiding, they surround themselves with powerful artifacts and ancient treasures. These items remind the Sith of their dark side identity, but appear harmless to others. The Sith also make use of sophisticated equipment on their evil missions. Beware!

KEY

1. ELECTROBINOCULARS with target locator for tracking enemies.

2. HOLOCRON stores ancient Sith data, which can be accessed only through use of the Force.

3. Compact, undetectable TRACER BEACON for tracking enemies.

4. Synthetic LIGHTSABER CRYSTAL to power Sith lightsabers.

5. FUNCTION CONTROL BELT regulates life-supporting armor and mask. Used by Darth Vader.

6. LIGHTSABER for use during duels.

7. WRIST LINK for remote control of probe droids. Also able to arm traps and detonate bombs.

8. BLACK CANE gives its owner the appearance of weakness. Darth Sidious carries it when he is Emperor.

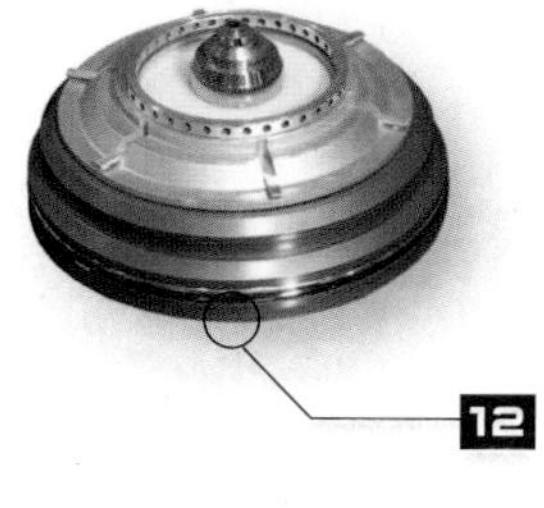

9. Statue of the ancient Dwartii Sage BRAATA, who encouraged the study of the dark side.

10. HOLOGRAM WATCH for communicating with Sith Master via hologram.

11. SITH CHALICE holds rare Korribanian incense, which is used in Sith rituals.

12. Compact, desk-mounted HOLOPROJECTOR for displaying hologram transmissions.

13. FORCE DISPERSER for concealing a Sith presence in the Force. Sidious places this on his desk in the Chancellor's office.

14. MEDICAL KIT contains life-saving potions and equipment.

15. Ornate SPIRIT URN to hold objects of importance.

16. Ancient BANE STATUE rotates to identify nearby Force users.

10

11

12

13

14

15

16

FIERCE WARRIOR
Darth Maul's character was forged from an early age to be cruel. Darth Sidious spotted useful potential in Maul when he was an infant, and trained him secretly in the dark side. The young Sith learned to have no mercy and show no fear.

Darth MAUL

Thanks to his mastery of martial arts and his deadly saberstaff, Darth Maul is a fearsome opponent. His brief duel with Qui-Gon on Tatooine further fans the flames of his hatred, and he lusts to finish off the Jedi Master.

After millennia of silence, the Sith reemerge with the appearance of Darth Maul on Tatooine. Strong in the Force and skilful with a lightsaber, this mysterious Sith is a dangerous dark side warrior.

SITH STATS

SPECIES: ZABRAK
HOMEWORLD: DATHOMIR
BIRTHDATE: 54 BBY
HEIGHT: 5 FT 9 IN (1.75 M)
TRAINED BY: DARTH SIDIOUS
WEAPONS: DOUBLE-BLADED RED LIGHTSABER (SABERSTAFF)
TRADEMARK: MARTIAL ARTS

BLACK AND RED TATTOOS COVER ENTIRE BODY

YELLOW IRIS

DEDICATED ZABRAK

As a Zabrak, Maul is a humanoid creature with horns and distinctive facial tattoos particular to the Nightbrothers clan of Dathomir. A proud and confident species, Zabraks are known for their single-mindedness, which Maul brings to his study of the dark side.

PRIDE BEFORE A FALL

Maul is a master of lightsaber combat, but his overconfidence is his downfall. When he duels two Jedi Knights on Naboo, the Sith defeats Qui-Gon Jinn, only to fall to Qui-Gon's Padawan, Obi-Wan Kenobi.

WHAT HAPPENS WHEN ONE SITH TAKES ON TWO JEDI?

DARTH MAUL IS highly skilled and well trained. He does not hesitate to engage two Jedi in battle in the Theed Generator Complex. Maul demonstrates his agility and lightsaber prowess during the duel, although he is unable to defeat both Jedi at once. But Maul proves how deadly he is by separating his opponents and taking them on one at a time.

BATTLE PLAN

Darth Maul is confident that he can defeat both Jedi with his double-bladed lightsaber. He uses his Force skills to sense where his opponents will strike next.

DIVIDE AND CONQUER

During the battle, Darth Maul forces his opponents through a security hallway. When the laser doors separate Qui-Gon from Obi-Wan, Maul knows it's the perfect time to strike. Despite Qui-Gon's skill, Maul's strength overwhelms him and the noble Jedi is defeated.

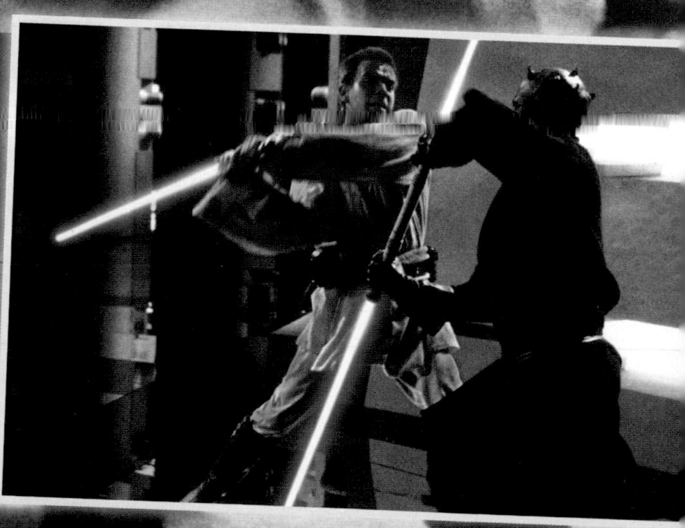

DOWNFALL

Enraged by the murder of his Master, Obi-Wan charges at Darth Maul. Although Obi-Wan's anger almost leads to his downfall, the Jedi summons all of his Force strength for a final attack on Maul, eventually defeating the Sith.

DARTH MAUL: LIGHTSABER COMBAT

Wielding a double-bladed saberstaff means that Darth Maul must choose his battle style carefully. The deadly Sith apprentice has developed his own unique form of lightsaber combat, which takes advantage of his strength and agility—and makes him almost unbeatable.

Darth Maul trained in the lightsaber combat form Juyo, which allows him to use his natural athletic abilities in battle. Using martial arts during a duel gives Maul the advantage of surprise. He also studies the style Niman, which focuses on balance, specifically for combat with dual blades.

LIGHTSABER WORKINGS

A Sith lightsaber is built very differently to a Jedi's. There is less emphasis on safety—and more focus on raw power.

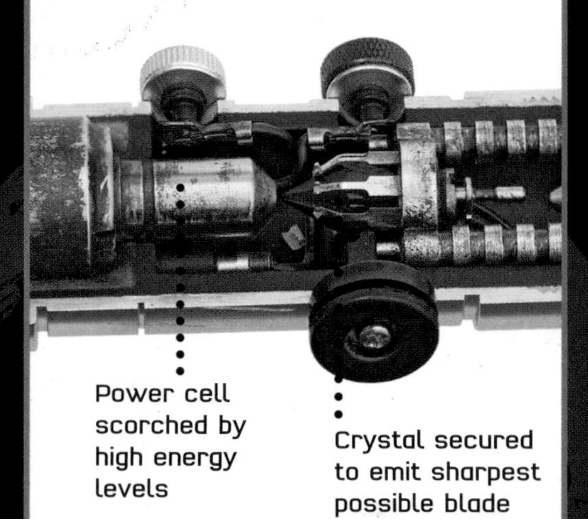

FORCE FIGHTING

Maul draws on dangerous dark side emotions to increase his power in battle. During a duel, he goes into a trance-like state where he is intensely focused on his saberstaff: he is able to visualize both blades of his lightsaber at once.

The saberstaff can break apart in the middle, forming two single-bladed lightsabers

Maul built his lightsaber using plans from an ancient Sith Holocron

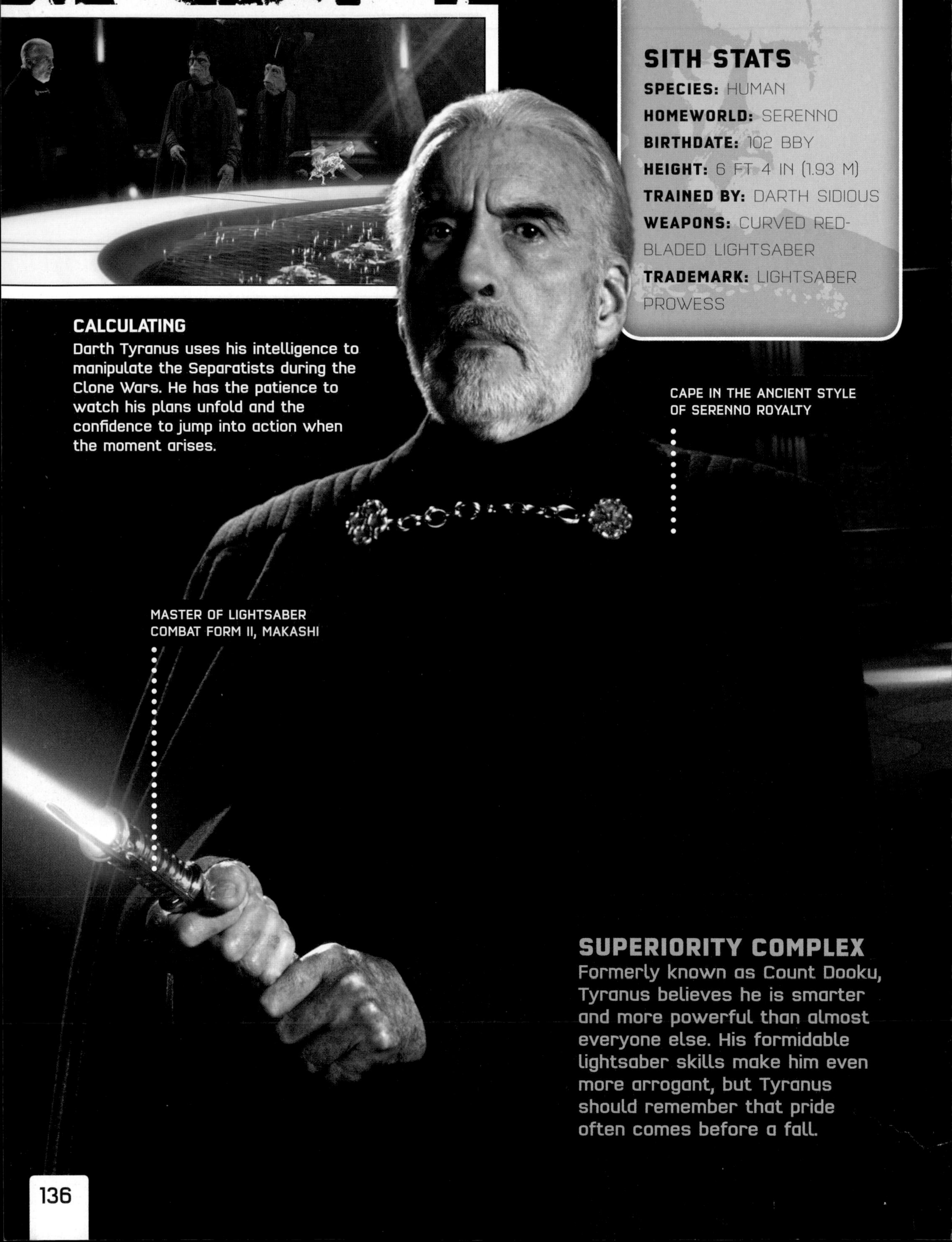

SITH STATS

SPECIES: HUMAN
HOMEWORLD: SERENNO
BIRTHDATE: 102 BBY
HEIGHT: 6 FT 4 IN (1.93 M)
TRAINED BY: DARTH SIDIOUS
WEAPONS: CURVED RED-BLADED LIGHTSABER
TRADEMARK: LIGHTSABER PROWESS

CALCULATING

Darth Tyranus uses his intelligence to manipulate the Separatists during the Clone Wars. He has the patience to watch his plans unfold and the confidence to jump into action when the moment arises.

CAPE IN THE ANCIENT STYLE OF SERENNO ROYALTY

MASTER OF LIGHTSABER COMBAT FORM II, MAKASHI

SUPERIORITY COMPLEX

Formerly known as Count Dooku, Tyranus believes he is smarter and more powerful than almost everyone else. His formidable lightsaber skills make him even more arrogant, but Tyranus should remember that pride often comes before a fall.

SEARCHING FOR POWER
Count Dooku sincerely wants to combat corruption in the Senate, but his quest has led him down a path to the dark side. Dooku used to be a Jedi Master, but his ambition was his downfall. He joined the Sith and became Darth Tyranus because the dark side offered him more power.

Despite his deadly lightsaber skills, Darth Tyranus is no match for his former Master Yoda when they duel on Geonosis.

Darth TYRANUS

As leader of the Separatists, Darth Tyranus answers to no one but his Sith Master, Darth Sidious. Tyranus implements his master's evil plans, spreading war across the galaxy, confident that he is Sidious's only trusted servant. But Tyranus will soon learn never to trust a Sith.

DARTH VADER

LASER CANNON ABLE TO DESTROY AN ASTEROID

TIE ADVANCED X1

- **SIZE** 30 ft (9.2 m) long
- **MAX ACCELERATION** 4,150 G
- **CAPACITY** 1 pilot
- **WEAPONS** 2 laser cannons

BENT SOLAR ARRAY WINGS

SUPER STAR DESTROYER, *EXECUTOR*

- **SIZE** 62,336 ft (19,000 m) long
- **MAX ACCELERATION** 1,230 G
- **CAPACITY** 279,144 crew, 38,000 passengers
- **WEAPONS** 5,000 turbolaser and ion cannons, 250 concussion missile batteries, 40 tractor beam projectors

IMPOSING COMMAND TOWER

HANGAR BAY CAN HOLD THOUSANDS OF STARFIGHTERS

DARTH MAUL

SITH INFILTRATOR, *SCIMITAR*

- **SIZE** 87 ft (26.5 m) long
- **MAX ACCELERATION** 3,730 G
- **CAPACITY** 1 pilot, 6 passengers
- **WEAPONS** 6 solar ionisation panels, ion drive array

CLOAKING DEVICE ALLOWS MAUL TO TRAVEL UNNOTICED

AUTO-BRAKE SYSTEM IF STEERING COLUMN IS RELEASED

LOW CENTER OF GRAVITY

WINGS FOLD UPON LANDING

SITH SPEEDER, *BLOODFIN*

- **SIZE** 5 ft 6 in (1.65 m) long
- **SPEED** 404 mph (650 km/h)
- **CAPACITY** 1 pilot
- **WEAPONS** None

Speeders and STARSHIPS

Whether they are tracking a nearby Jedi, traveling to a clandestine meeting, or attacking a secret Rebel base, the Sith have many vehicles at their disposal. From one-person speeders and stealthy starships to enormous Imperial warships, each Sith selects his vehicle depending on his mission.

DARTH SIDIOUS

COMMUNICATIONS GRID

IMPERIAL SHUTTLE

- **SIZE** 66 ft (650 km/h) long
- **MAX ACCELERATION** 1,400 G
- **CAPACITY** 6 crew, 20 passengers
- **WEAPONS** 2 twin laser cannons, 1 twin blaster cannon

LOWER WINGS FOLD UP FOR LANDING

TIE FIGHTER HANGARS

DARTH TYRANUS

GEONOSIAN SPEEDER

- **SIZE** 10 ft 7 in (3.2 m) long
- **SPEED** 394 mph (634 km/h)
- **CAPACITY** 1 pilot
- **WEAPONS** None

CAN CLIMB TO ALTITUDE OF 1.2 MILES (2 KM) HIGH

SOLAR SAILER

- **SIZE** 55 ft (16.8 m) long, 345 ft (105.2 m) with sail open
- **MAX ACCELERATION** 1,000 G
- **CAPACITY** 3 crew, 1 passenger
- **WEAPONS** 84 miniature tractor-repulsor projectors

UNIQUE SAIL FROM GREE ENCLAVE

FLOWN BY FA-4 PILOT DROID

WHAT HONOR IS THERE AMONG THE SITH?

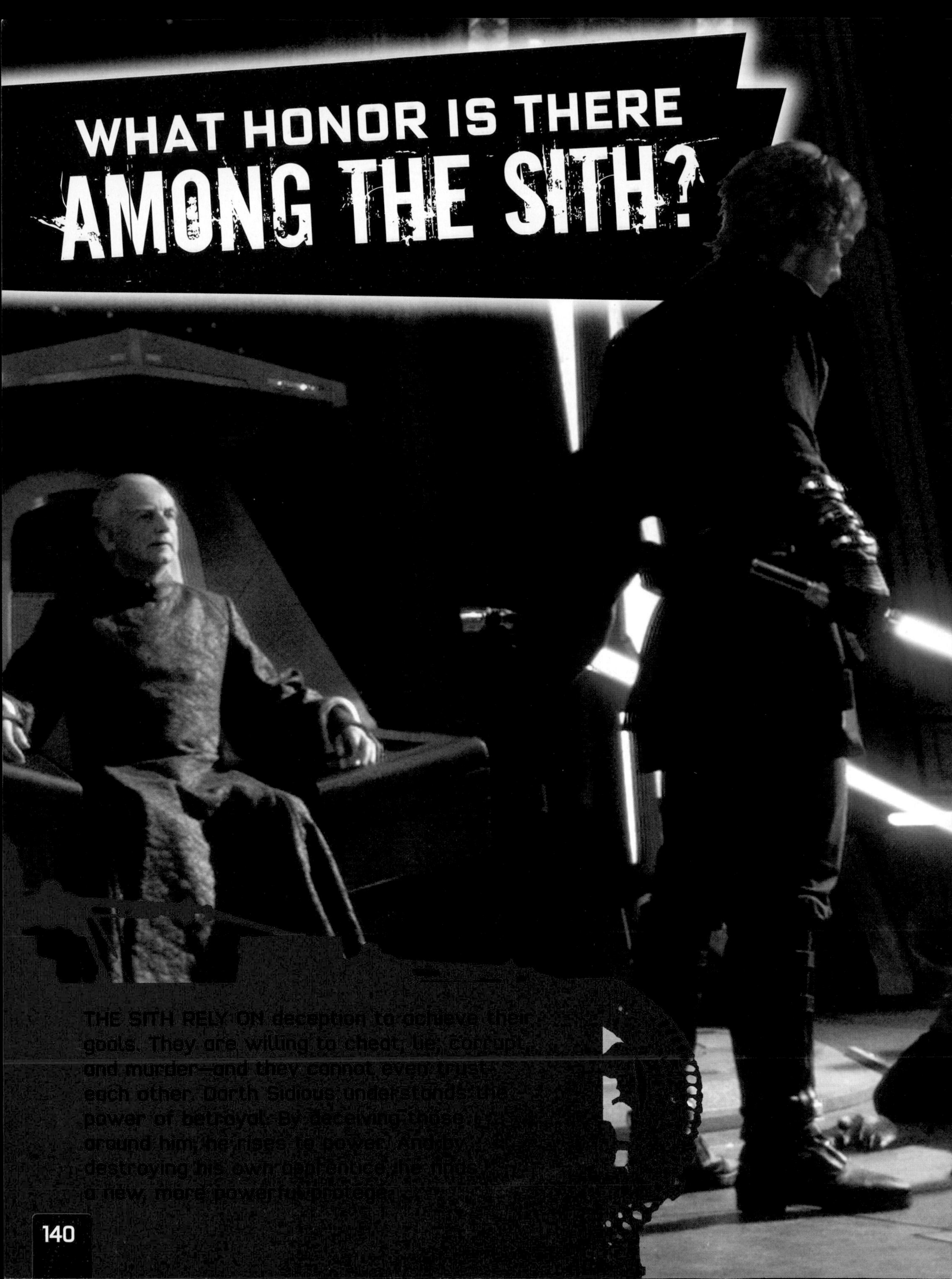

THE SITH RELY ON deception to achieve their goals. They are willing to cheat, lie, corrupt, and murder—and they cannot even trust each other. Darth Sidious understands the power of betrayal. By deceiving those around him, he rises to power. And by destroying his own apprentice, he finds a new, more powerful protégé.

PLAYING WITH LIVES

Darth Sidious feels no guilt for placing others in danger: he cares only for his own plans. When Sidious wants to judge whether Anakin is vulnerable to the dark side, he fakes his own kidnapping and calls the Jedi to his rescue. Anakin and Obi-Wan risk their lives, while Palpatine remains safe all along.

MINDLESS VIOLENCE

The Sith are willing to destroy innocent lives. Darth Vader and Grand Moff Tarkin assure Rebel leader Princess Leia that they will not destroy her home planet, Alderaan—but the Sith don't honor their promises. They proceed to test their new superweapon, the Death Star, on Alderaan, destroying the peaceful planet completely.

LACK OF LOYALTY

Darth Sidious shows no loyalty—even to his own apprentice, Darth Tyranus. Sidious instructs Anakin to destroy Tyranus, simply to see whether the young Jedi will obey. Anakin's obedience proves that he can be turned to the dark side.

SEPARATIST ARMY

Darth Tyranus, masquerading as Separatist leader Count Dooku, convinces Nute Gunray and Poggle the Lesser to built an enormous Droid Army in the factories of Geonosis.

The Separatist war room on the lava planet Mustafar is a flurry of military activity. Darth Sidious sends his orders via hologram, while Separatist officers and battle droids implement Droid Army strategy using control panels and long-distance comlinks.

POGGLE THE LESSER

ARCHDUKE

Poggle the Lesser is the Archduke of Geonosis and a senior member of the Separatist Council. Following his successful creation of the Droid Army, Poggle now commands hives of Geonosians in a top-secret project for Darth Tyranus.

COMMAND STAFF MADE FROM THE BONES OF A MURDERED POLITICAL OPPONENT

COLLECTION OF STOLEN LIGHTSABERS FROM JEDI VICTIMS IS CONCEALED WITHIN CLOAK

HUMAN ORGANS ENCASED IN ROBOTIC BODY

GENERAL GRIEVOUS

SUPREME COMMANDER
General Grievous was chosen to command the Droid Army because of his savage reputation. The cyborg's hatred for the Jedi is an added bonus.

Allies of the SITH

The Separatists want to break away from Republic rule. They have joined forces with the Sith and built a fearsome Droid Army. But in pursuit of independence, their aggressive and violent tactics quickly raise alarm.

SEPARATISTS

LEADER: COUNT DOOKU

ALLEGIANCE: SITH

HEADQUARTERS: RAXUS

WEAPONS: DROID ARMY

VALUES: INDEPENDENCE, MILITARY POWER

SITH STRATEGY: CLONE WARS

Darth Sidious is secretly in control of both the Republic and the Separatists. He uses his powerful position to spark the Clone Wars, during which he plays both sides against each other, hoping to destroy all opposition and assume complete control of the galaxy. The Sith Lord carries out his Clone Wars battle plan, reveling in the chaos he creates.

1. BUILD A SECRET ARMY

OBJECTIVE:
Create an army for the Republic, which is secretly loyal to the Sith.

OUTCOME:
The Clone Army is deployed by the Republic. Jedi Generals fight alongside clone troopers, unaware of their true allegiance.
MISSION COMPLETE.

2. GAIN TRUST OF THE JEDI

OBJECTIVE:
Palpatine to avoid suspicion and remain involved in the plans of the Jedi.

OUTCOME:
The Jedi trust Chancellor Palpatine and discuss political matters and military strategy with him.
MISSION COMPLETE.

3. TAKE CONTROL OF CLONE ARMY

OBJECTIVE:
Darth Sidious to activate Order 66 and place the Clone Army under Sith control.

OUTCOME:
Order 66 initiated successfully, commanding clone troopers to destroy the Jedi. The resulting Jedi Purge wipes out almost every Jedi and Padawan.
MISSION COMPLETE.

"I have good news for you, my lord. **WAR HAS BEGUN.**"

Darth Tyranus

4. DESTROY THE JEDI ORDER

OBJECTIVE:
Destroy the Jedi Order once and for all.

OUTCOME:
The Jedi Temple, home to the Jedi Order, is destroyed. The few surviving Jedi are forced to flee into exile. MISSION INCOMPLETE.

5. OBLITERATE THE SEPARATISTS

OBJECTIVE:
Destroy all obstacles to total control.

OUTCOME:
New apprentice Darth Vader sent to annihilate the Separatist Council. No governing body remains to oppose Sidious's takeover of the Senate and galaxy. MISSION COMPLETE.

6. RULE THE GALAXY

OBJECTIVE:
Sidious to become sole ruler of the galaxy.

OUTCOME:
Sidious blames a Jedi plot for the fall of the Republic. He declares that the Republic will become a Galactic Empire—and he will rule as Emperor. MISSION COMPLETE.

CONSEQUENCES:

The galaxy is plunged into darkness after the Clone Wars. With the surviving Jedi forced into exile, there is no stopping Sidious from assuming the role of Emperor. The Sith Lord now has total control of the galaxy.

WHAT HAPPENS WHEN THE SITH START A WAR?

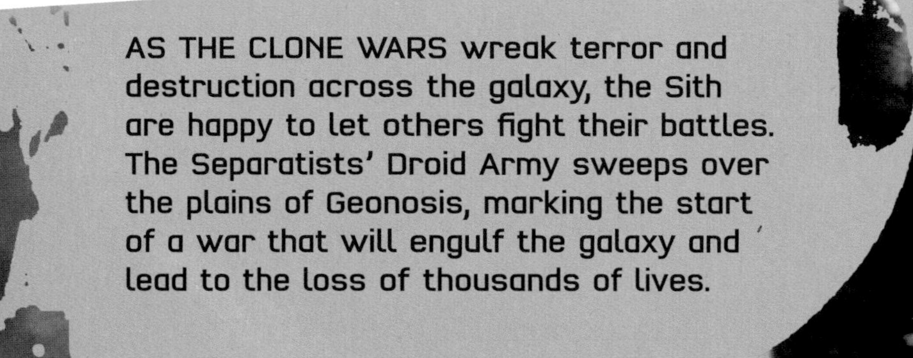

AS THE CLONE WARS wreak terror and destruction across the galaxy, the Sith are happy to let others fight their battles. The Separatists' Droid Army sweeps over the plains of Geonosis, marking the start of a war that will engulf the galaxy and lead to the loss of thousands of lives.

JEDI GENERALS
As the Clone Wars begin, the Jedi lead the Clone Army in battle. Although the Jedi Order usually prefers negotiation to combat, the Clone Wars present them with a choice: fight to protect their values... or accept the actions of the Sith.

SITH COMMANDER

As they march across Geonosis, the soldiers and machines of the Droid Army receive orders from the Trade Federation. These orders, in turn, come from Darth Tyranus, their lord and master.

DESTRUCTION

The Clone Wars draw to a close following Order 66, and the Jedi must accept their defeat. The Sith have triumphed and Darth Sidious has turned the Republic into his Empire. As the Jedi Temple burns, the surviving Jedi go into hiding.

CLONES CAN SOMETIMES THINK FOR THEMSELVES

CLONE TROOPER

The Clone Army fights for the Republic during the Clone Wars, but the troopers are not what they seem. They have been programmed with Order 66, a secret command to attack their Jedi comrades. As soon as Darth Sidious activates the order, the entire Clone Army will be under Sith control.

TRAINED AS SOLDIERS SINCE CHILDHOOD

POWERFUL DC-15A BLASTER RIFLE

SOLDIERS OF THE SITH

Huge armies are controlled by the Sith, tasked with enforcing their laws and fighting their battles. Following the Clone Wars, Darth Sidious commands millions of soldiers from both the Republic and Separatist militaries. The soldiers are obedient and relentless—a deadly combination, especially when they are programmed to enforce the evil orders of the Sith.

REMOTE CONNECTION TO CONTROL SHIP

SUPERB AIM

ABLE TO RUN LONG DISTANCES WITHOUT TIRING

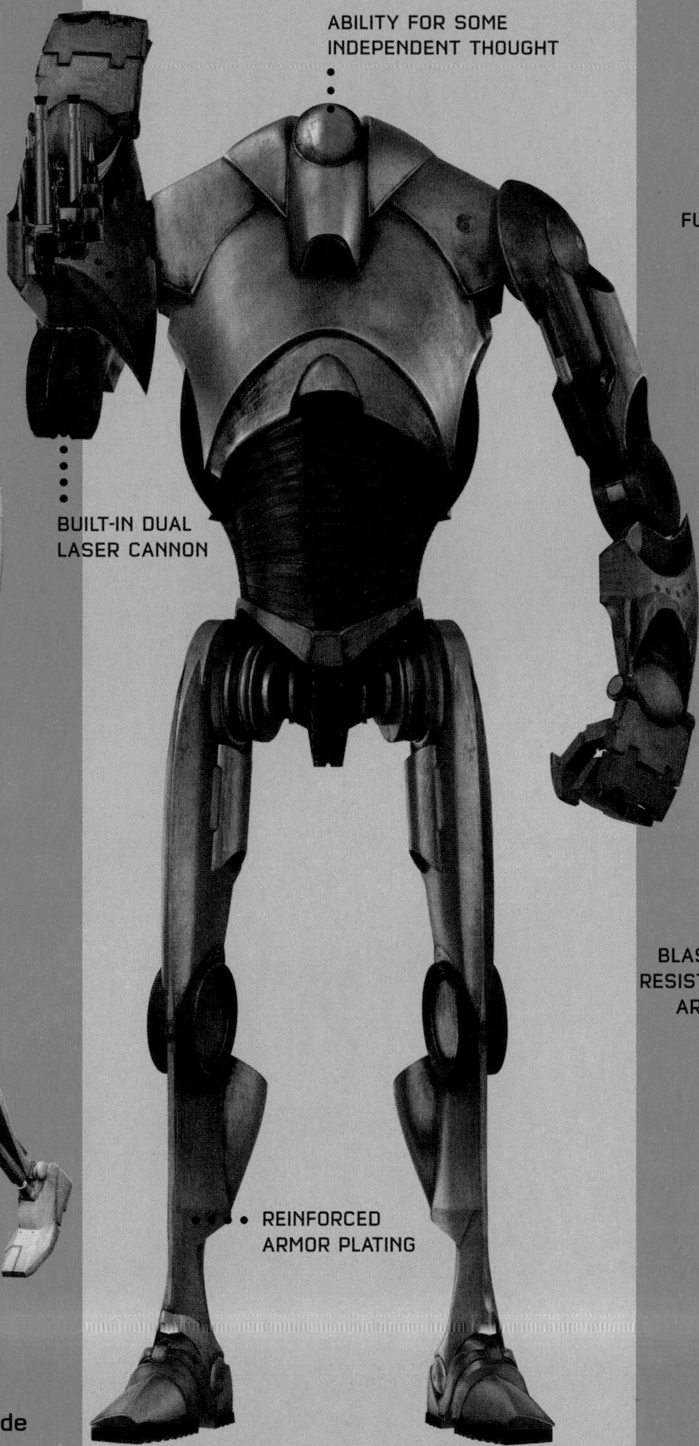

ABILITY FOR SOME INDEPENDENT THOUGHT

BUILT-IN DUAL LASER CANNON

REINFORCED ARMOR PLATING

FULLY INDEPENDENT THOUGHT

FULL COMLINK IN HELMET

BLASTER RESISTANT ARMOR

BATTLE DROID

Darth Sidious and Darth Tyranus employ the Trade Federation to build an enormous Droid Army. Millions of battle droids swarm across the galaxy during the Clone Wars, on a mission to defeat the Republic.

SUPER BATTLE DROID

Super battle droids are upgraded droid soldiers. They join regular battle droids on the battlefield during the Clone Wars, mindlessly obeying the orders of their Sith-serving controllers.

STORMTROOPER

Once Darth Sidious becomes Emperor, he transforms the Clone Army into the mighty Imperial Army. Stormtroopers patrol every corner of the galaxy, ensuring that Sith law is obeyed without question.

WHAT HAPPENS WHEN A SITH IS EXPOSED?

DARTH SIDIOUS HAS been masquerading as Supreme Chancellor Palpatine for many years, but it is only a matter of time until his betrayal is discovered. When the Jedi realize that their nemesis is actually the Supreme Chancellor, Mace Windu leads a team of Jedi Masters to arrest the Sith Lord. The Jedi are armed with lightsabers, well aware that a Sith will not surrender quietly.

CONFRONTATION

Darth Sidious is quick to react when confronted. He reveals his hidden lightsaber and displays his deadly Sith powers by destroying Jedi Saesee Tiin, Agen Kolar, and Kit Fisto in a matter of seconds.

ATTACK

Darth Sidious then turns his lightsaber on Mace Windu. But the Jedi demonstrates his deadly Vaapad combat skills and pushes Sidious to the brink of defeat.

CHOOSING SIDES

Mace is about to deal the fatal blow when Anakin Skywalker appears. Sidious seizes the opportunity to turn Anakin to the dark side once and for all: he pretends he is too weak to defend himself and begs Anakin to save him. Anakin makes a quick decision. He cuts off Mace's lightsaber hand, giving Sidious the chance to destroy Mace with Sith lightning.

“I HAD A DREAM THAT I WAS A JEDI.”
ANAKIN SKYWALKER

“HE DESERVES BETTER THAN A SLAVE’S LIFE.”
SHMI SKYWALKER

“THERE’S SOMETHING ABOUT THIS BOY.”
QUI-GON JINN

“THE FORCE IS UNUSUALLY STRONG WITH HIM.”
QUI-GON JINN

“HE WILL NOT LET ME DOWN. HE NEVER HAS.”
OBI-WAN KENOBI

“THERE IS GOOD IN HIM. I’VE FELT IT.”
LUKE SKYWALKER

> "I'M NOT THE JEDI I SHOULD BE. I WANT MORE—BUT I KNOW I SHOULDN'T."
>
> ANAKIN SKYWALKER

> "I DON'T TRUST HIM."
>
> MACE WINDU

> "TWISTED BY THE DARK SIDE, YOUNG SKYWALKER HAS BECOME."
>
> YODA

> "THE BOY IS DANGEROUS."
>
> OBI-WAN KENOBI

> "THE FORCE IS STRONG WITH YOU! A POWERFUL SITH, YOU WILL BECOME."
>
> DARTH SIDIOUS

THE DARKNESS WITHIN

Anakin Skywalker was always expected to do great things. His connection with the Force meant that he became the greatest Jedi the galaxy had ever seen. Yet, even from a young age, Anakin's soul was in turmoil. He often wants more. Is his fall to the dark side inevitable?

Following a brutal duel against Obi-Wan Kenobi, Vader's human body was almost completely destroyed. Life-supporting armor now conceals all that remains of Anakin Skywalker.

BETRAYED BY EMOTION
Vader used to be Anakin Skywalker, a famous Jedi Knight, but he was never able to overcome his negative emotions. He feared the death of his wife, Padmé, and was turned to the dark side by Darth Sidious who exploited his feelings.

Darth VADER

Sith apprentice Darth Vader is the leader of the Imperial Army. He seeks to crush the Rebellion against his Master, the Emperor. Vader will not tolerate weakness and shows no mercy—even to his own troops.

SITH STATS

SPECIES: HUMAN
HOMEWORLD: TATOOINE
BIRTHDATE: 41 BBY
HEIGHT: 2.02 M (6 FT 8 IN)
TRAINED BY: DARTH SIDIOUS
WEAPONS: RED-BLADED LIGHTSABER
TRADEMARK: FORCE CHOKE

DURASTEEL ARMOR
PROTECTS MOBILE
LIFE-SUPPORT SYSTEM

RESPIRATORY DEVICE
AMPLIFIES BREATHING
SOUNDS

FORCE CONNECTION

Darth Vader has strong Force powers, which make him an expert pilot and lightsaber combatant. He also uses the Force to sense the feelings of those around him, giving him a constant advantage over others.

FATHER AND SON

Darth Vader senses many similarities between himself and his son, Luke Skywalker. He tries to convince Luke to become his Sith apprentice, so father and son can overthrow the Emperor and rule together.

CAN A SITH DEFEAT HIS FORMER JEDI MASTER?

WHEN A JEDI turns to the dark side, the Jedi Order is forever haunted by the loss. A fallen Jedi is a great threat because he knows the secrets of the Order and has been trained in the light side of the Force. So, when a fallen Jedi battles his former Jedi Master, their shared history can become a powerful weapon.

KNOW YOUR ENEMY

When Darth Tyranus faces Yoda on the planet Geonosis, the Sith uses his knowledge of Yoda's Jedi values to escape. He forces Yoda to make a choice: defeat Tyranus or save Anakin and Obi-Wan from being crushed.

LIGHT VS DARK

Yoda is troubled to learn that Count Dooku has chosen the dark side. He is determined to stop the former Jedi, no matter how powerful he has become.

OLD FRIENDS

On Mustafar, the newly created Sith Lord Darth Vader attacks his former friend and Jedi Master, Obi-Wan Kenobi. Vader calls on the dark side to harness more power, but he is overwhelmed by rage. Obi-Wan takes advantage of Darth Vader's weaknesses and defeats him.

SACRIFICE

Many years later, Obi-Wan and Darth Vader duel for a second time. The Sith Lord is now more experienced and powerful. However, the Jedi knows something that Vader does not—that there is life beyond death. Obi-Wan submits to Vader's death blow, so that Luke and the Rebels can escape—and that he may continue to teach Luke.

Rebellion against the SITH

In a galaxy obedient to the Sith, few are brave enough to resist. The Rebel Alliance aims to restore the galaxy to its former state as a democratic Republic and to end the terrible dictatorship of the Sith and their Empire.

The Rebels are willing to die for their cause. They protect their Echo Base headquarters on Hoth against invading Imperial troops, even though they are vastly outnumbered.

REBEL WITH A CAUSE

Princess Leia Organa is the Empire's youngest and most determined Senator. She is on a mission to destroy the Death Star and the danger it poses.

THE LAST JEDI

Luke Skywalker is astonished to learn he has Force powers. He begins his Jedi training and joins the Rebel Alliance. Luke is determined to destroy the Sith and learn the truth about his father.

REBEL ALLIANCE

LEADER: MON MOTHMA

ALLEGIANCE: REBEL ALLIANCE

HEADQUARTERS: *HOME ONE*

WEAPONS: DH-17 BLASTER PISTOL, A280 BLASTER RIFLE

VALUES: DEMOCRACY, FREEDOM

QUICK ON THE DRAW, HAN SOLO IS GOOD IN A DUEL

HONORABLE SMUGGLER

Han Solo didn't intend to join the Rebel Alliance, but he proves an invaluable pilot when he chooses to join his friends in their fight against the Sith.

LUKE SKYWALKER

HAN SOLO

REBEL MIGHT

The Rebel Fleet is small but dangerous. Flying their one-seater B-wings, X-wings, and Y-wings, Rebel pilots defeat the enormous ships of the Imperial Navy, thanks to careful planning, impressive skill, and plenty of courage.

DL-44 BLASTER PISTOL

SUPERWEAPONS

The Force is more powerful than any weapon, but it can't be seen or touched. Darth Sidious wants to create a physical symbol of his immense power to strike fear into the hearts of everyone in the galaxy. The Sith Lord orders the construction of a huge, mobile battle station called the Death Star, which has enough firepower to destroy an entire planet. Even when the Death Star is destroyed by Rebel forces, Sidious uses the might and resources of the Empire to build a second, even more terrifying Death Star.

MAIN POWER GENERATOR

HYPERMATTER REACTOR

DEATH STAR I

- **SIZE** 160 km (99 miles) diameter
- **HYPERDRIVE RATING** Class 4.0
- **MAXIMUM SPEED** 10 MGLT
- **SUPERLASER RECHARGE** 24 hours
- **COMBAT VEHICLES** 11,000
- **PERSONNEL** 1.7 million

DEATH STAR II

- **SIZE** 900 km (550 miles) diameter
- **HYPERDRIVE RATING** Class 3.0
- **MAXIMUM SPEED** 20 MGLT
- **SUPERLASER RECHARGE** 3 minutes
- **COMBAT VEHICLES** 25,000
- **PERSONNEL** 2.5 million

LASER STATIONS READY!

When the hypermatter reactor is fully charged, the superlaser is ready to be deployed. Beams of energy from eight separate laser stations converge on the surface of the Death Star's lens to produce the primary beam.

SUPERLASER POWER CELL

HYPERDRIVE

CENTRAL COMPUTER CORE

DEATH STAR II

The second Death Star is bigger than the first—and promises to be even more deadly. When the Rebels attempt to destroy it, Darth Sidious decides to demonstrate its power.

The superlaser is precise enough to aim at a moving target. Its primary beam strikes a Rebel starfighter, destroying it in seconds, leaving the Rebels in no doubt as to the strength of their Imperial enemies.

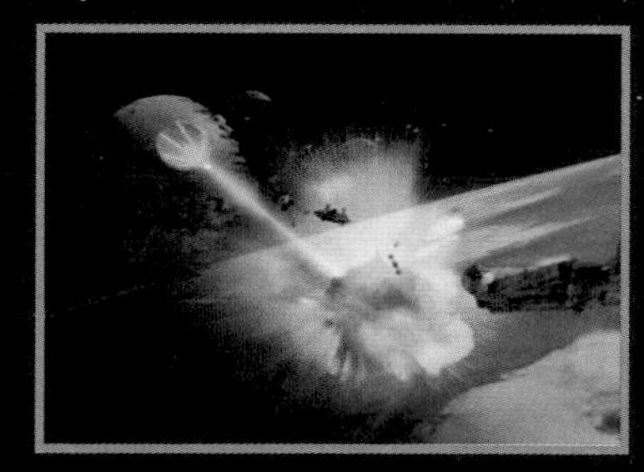

SITH SECRETS

■ The Death Star plans were drawn up by the Separatists during the Clone Wars. Darth Sidious hid them until he had the power to begin construction.

A SITH AMONG THEM

Most Imperial soldiers remain unaware that the Emperor is a Sith Lord. Darth Sidious is rarely seen by the Imperial troops, although he often sends his apprentice Darth Vader to inspect the progress of his military projects.

OFFICER'S DISC

IMPERIAL CODE CYLINDER

LIEUTENANT SHECKIL

FEAR OF FAILURE

During a mission to Cloud City, Lieutenant Sheckil is Darth Vader's second-in-command. When Sheckil fails to complete his assignment, he worries that he might have to face the legendary wrath of Darth Vader.

SECRET DATA STORED IN BELT BUCKLE DISC

Even small, out-of-the-way planets like Tatooine must submit to Imperial patrols. Sandtroopers search the desert on dewback mounts, keeping an eye out for their quarry.

IMPERIAL ARMY

LEADER: EMPEROR PALPATINE
ALLEGIANCE: EMPIRE
HEADQUARTERS: CORUSCANT
WEAPONS: E-11 BLASTER RIFLE, THERMAL DETONATOR
VALUES: IMPERIAL LAW, OBEDIENCE

Army OF THE EMPIRE

The Imperial military has a fearsome reputation. Charged with enforcing Emperor Palpatine's laws, armor-clad stormtroopers patrol the far reaches of the galaxy. As Emperor, Darth Sidious issues orders from his Throne Room, intent on destroying the Rebellion.

INTERROGATION DROID

IT-O

Just one look at this fearsome hovering droid is usually enough to make prisoners talk. The IT-O contains many dangerous tools and deadly functions that are designed to scare prisoners into revealing any hidden secrets to their captors.

PROTOCOL DROID

RA-7

Built to serve high-ranking Imperial officers, this protocol droid is also equipped with a secret surveillance system, so he can spy on his surroundings.

MOUSE DROID

MSE-6

These droids are used exclusively by the Imperial Navy. They perform simple tasks, such as delivering messages and escorting troops around the Death Star.

ASTROMECH DROID

R2-Q5

Stationed on the second Death Star, R2-Q5 performs normal astromech duties such as repairing starships, but he is also equipped with hidden spy devices.

Sith **DROIDS**

Droids are used across the galaxy for many purposes. The Sith often have unique requirements for their droids, so they have been known to commission their own designs, or update already existing models to use for their wicked purposes.

PROBE DROIDS

DRK-1

Darth Maul's Dark Eye probe droid was designed using plans from a Sith Holocron. It features a long-distance transmission antenna and a stealth mechanism that enables it to avoid detection.

VIPER PROBE

Sent across the galaxy to track targets for the Imperial Army, the Viper probe droid is a less specialized model than the Dark Eye. It is equipped with weapons and a self-destruct device.

MEDICAL DROIDS

TRIPEDAL MEDDROIDS

Designed by Darth Sidious, these three-legged assistant droids have specially designed arms that can operate with incredible precision.

FX-6

This medical assistant droid helps repair Darth Vader's body after his duel with Obi-Wan on Mustafar. He has seven multi-functional upper arms and 13 lower arms, as well as many vials of medical fluids, such as bacta.

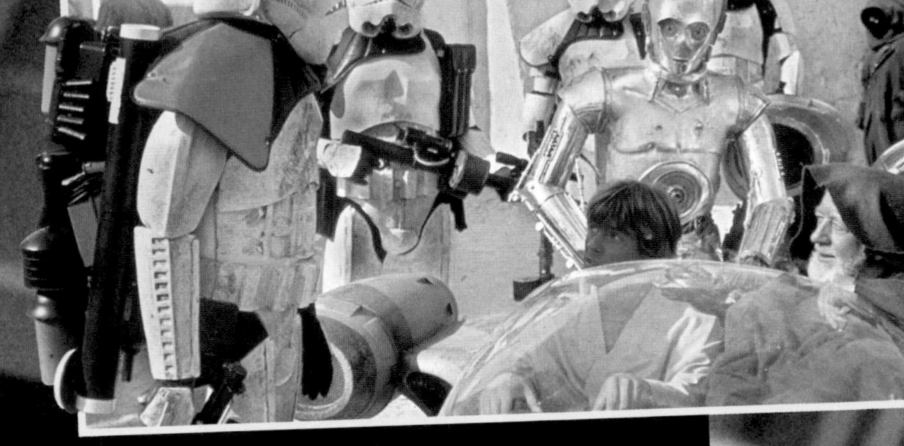

NOWHERE TO HIDE
The Sith extend their influence by deploying Imperial commanders and their troops to thousands of distant planets. Carrying out Sith orders and policing galactic citizens, the stormtroopers are feared as an extension of their power. Few people dare to disobey.

HOW DO THE SITH MAINTAIN CONTROL?

THERE ARE ONLY EVER two Sith, so to control an entire galaxy, they must use all their cunning. By crafting a terrifying reputation, the Sith use fear to keep order. They shroud themselves in mystery and encourage rumors that inspire dread in all who hear them. The Sith ensure everyone knows that they don't tolerate weakness. They don't forgive and they never forget.

UNFORGIVING

Darth Vader instills terror in his own troops to keep them under control. His punishment for an officer's mistake is death by Force choke.

SHROUDED IN SECRECY

Darth Sidious establishes a fearsome reputation among his own officers, even Darth Vader. He keeps his visits to the Death Star to a minimum, so that when he does appear—half-concealed by his black cloak—he is surrounded by an air of awe and terror. Imperial officers are terrified of his wrath.

HIRED HELP

LEADER: NONE

ALLEGIANCE: WHOEVER OFFERS THE HIGHEST PRICE

WEAPONS: E-11 BLASTER RIFLE, THERMAL DETONATOR

VALUES: JOB COMPLETION, MONEY, BLASTER SKILLS

FACE CLOTH TO MASK ZAM'S FACE

BLENDING IN

Zam Wesell is a shapeshifting assassin, hired to destroy Padmé Amidala. Before Zam can complete her mission, she is caught by two Jedi Knights. About to identify her client, Zam is silenced with a saberdart—fired by bounty hunter Jango Fett.

SPECIAL FABRIC ALLOWS ZAM TO BLEND INTO SHADOWS

DENGAR
Remorseless killer

JETPACK CONTAINS ROCKET LAUNCHER

COMLINK

ZAM WESELL

RUTHLESS

Jango Fett is a superb marksman—and a top fighter even without his blaster. His tough armor and diverse collection of weaponry means you definitely don't want him on your trail!

JANGO FETT

JANGO FETT'S DNA IS USED TO CREATE THE CLONE ARMY

A BARGAIN WITH THE SITH

The Sith are powerful enough to force others to obey them. When Darth Vader tracks the Rebels to Cloud City, he makes a deal with Baron Administrator Lando Calrissian. If Lando hands over the Rebels, Cloud City will remain free from Imperial control. Lando agrees, although he later has second thoughts about aiding the Sith.

IG-88
Sadistic assassin

BOBA FETT
Deadly marksman

BOSSK
Vengeful hunter

4-LOM
Criminal droid

ZUCKUSS
Relentless tracker

Darth Vader is desperate to catch a small group of Rebels, so he employs the services of some of the most famous bounty hunters in the galaxy: Dengar, IG-88, Boba Fett, Bossk, 4-LOM, and Zuckuss.

Bounty HUNTERS

Sith Lords prefer to control events from a safe distance, and often hire others to do their work for them. To carry out dangerous tasks, such as catching their enemies, the Sith often turn to bounty hunters and assassins, who will take on any mission—no matter how evil—for a fee.

HOW POWERFUL IS A CYBORG HIRED BY THE SITH?

SUPREME COMMANDER of the Separatist Droid Army, General Grievous wields much power. His cyborg body is fast and strong, and he is fueled by a deep hatred of the Jedi. With the might of the Droid Army behind him, his ability to wield four lightsabers at once, and his renowned tactical skills, Grievous is one opponent who must not be underestimated.

BODY ARMOR

Injured by a bomb, General Grievous's living body was almost destroyed. His remains were built into a duranium shell, turning him into a cyborg. Now, Grievous's tough, metal body is one of his greatest strengths. The cyborg is able to withstand the crushing pressures of outer space when he escapes from the Jedi through the window of his starship, *Invisible Hand*.

SITH SECRETS

■ Grievous claims his transformation into a cyborg was by his own choice. But he doesn't realize that the bomb that destroyed his body was planted by Darth Tyranus as part of a plan to place Grievous under Sith control.

NO MATCH FOR A JEDI

Although the fearsome cyborg has been trained in the art of lightsaber combat by Darth Tyranus, he cannot fully harness the power of the dark side. When Grievous finally comes face to face with Obi-Wan Kenobi, he cannot match the Jedi's skills and is soon defeated.

SITH TARGET:

LUKE SKYWALKER

When Darth Vader discovers the existence of his son, Luke Skywalker, he embarks on a mission to recruit Luke to the dark side. Luke has begun his Jedi training, so Vader will need all his cunning and skill to turn his son into a Sith. Fortunately for Vader, he has all the resources of the Empire at his disposal...

1. LOCATE LUKE SKYWALKER

OBJECTIVE:
Imperial Army to discover the location of Rebel headquarters and capture Luke Skywalker.

OUTCOME:
Probe droids locate Echo Base headquarters on Hoth, but Luke and the Rebels escape.
MISSION INCOMPLETE.

2. THE LURE

OBJECTIVE:
Darth Vader to lure Luke to Cloud City by capturing his friends, Princess Leia and Han Solo.

OUTCOME:
Han Solo is frozen in carbonite and the others are captured. Luke arrives to rescue his friends, but is confronted by Vader.
MISSION COMPLETE.

"Join me, and **TOGETHER** we can rule the galaxy as **FATHER AND SON.**"

DARTH VADER

3. FIRST DUEL

OBJECTIVE:
Darth Vader to persuade Luke to become his Sith apprentice.

OUTCOME:
During a lightsaber duel, Vader reveals he is Luke's father. Luke refuses to join the dark side. MISSION FAILED.

4. THE POWER OF PERSUASION

OBJECTIVE:
Darth Vader to convince Luke to join forces with the Sith.

OUTCOME:
Luke comes to the Death Star voluntarily, but Vader is unable to persuade him to join the Sith. MISSION FAILED.

5. THREATEN FRIENDS

OBJECTIVE:
Force Luke to join the dark side in order to protect his allies.

OUTCOME:
Luke's friends are captured and threatened, but Luke has faith in the Rebels' mission and refuses to join the dark side. MISSION FAILED.

6. FINAL DUEL

OBJECTIVE:
Vader to turn Luke to the dark side—or destroy him.

OUTCOME:
Following a fierce duel with Vader, Luke is almost killed by the Emperor. But Vader finally returns to the light side and saves his son. MISSION FAILED.

CONSEQUENCES:

Darth Vader fails at almost every stage of his plan. Luke not only proves his dedication to the Jedi Order, but also manages to awaken the last remnants of his father Anakin Skywalker's humanity. Father and son are at last reunited—on the light side of the Force.

WHO WILL TRIUMPH WHEN A SITH DUELS HIS SON?

SITH AND JEDI WARRIORS have dueled many times over the centuries. But this time the fate of the galaxy hangs not just on a battle between the dark side and the light side—but on a battle between father and son. Although Darth Vader and Luke Skywalker are equally strong in the Force, their duels are more than just about physical strength. Strong emotions influence their battles, but whose will is stronger?

A SON'S ANGER

When Darth Vader first duels Luke, he senses much of himself in the young Jedi. He encourages Luke to release his anger in an effort to turn him to the dark side.

TRUTH REVEALED

On Cloud City, Darth Vader cuts off Luke's hand in battle, leaving the young Jedi at his mercy. But the Sith Lord's intentions are not what Luke expects! Instead of destroying the Jedi, Darth Vader tries to turn him to the dark side. In an effort to persuade Luke, Vader shocks him by revealing that he is Luke's father.

A FATHER'S LOVE

When Darth Vader and Luke duel a second time on the Death Star, their family bond affects both their decisions: each would rather recruit his opponent than destroy him. In the end, Luke's victory is sealed when Darth Vader returns to the light side of the Force and sacrifices himself to save the life of his son.

LIKE FATHER

In many ways, Jedi Luke Skywalker's life seems to be following a similar path to his father's. Although he never met the Jedi Anakin Skywalker, they have much in common. Can Luke use the light side of the Force to break the pattern and choose his own future? Only time will tell...

LATECOMER TO THE JEDI ORDER

Nine-year-old Anakin is a lot older than most younglings who begin their Jedi training. His special connection with the Force convinces the Jedi Order to train him.

Luke is 22 years old when he begins his Jedi training. No new Jedi have been trained since the Jedi Purge, but Yoda realizes that Luke offers new hope for the exiled Jedi Order.

EXCEPTIONALLY STRONG IN THE FORCE

Anakin's Force skills enable him to pilot his spaceship at incredible speeds. He is one of the most famous pilots in the Republic.

Luke uses his sharp Jedi reflexes to pilot his spaceship with skill. His connection with the Force enables him to destroy the Death Star.

"I AM A JEDI, LIKE MY FATHER BEFORE ME."

LUKE SKYWALKER

HAUNTED BY VISIONS

Anakin is haunted by nightmares and fears for the people he loves. He grows less and less able to control these emotions.

Luke's feelings cause him to have dark side visions during his Jedi training. He must overcome these thoughts if he wants to progress.

DISOBEDIENT

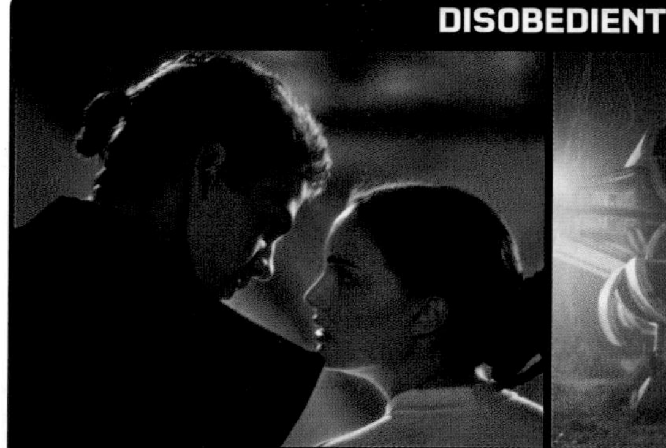

Anakin is a disobedient Padawan. He ignores many teachings of the Jedi Order, including the rule that a Jedi must not fall in love.

Luke refuses to heed Yoda's advice that he should complete his Jedi training. He rushes off to Cloud City, even though it is a trap.

SCARRED IN BATTLE

Anakin loses his right hand during a duel with Darth Tyranus. His injury serves as a reminder of his impatience and inexperience.

Luke's right hand is cut off by Darth Vader during their first duel. For Luke, the injury symbolizes his similarities to his father.

Luke does not try to escape his destiny. He knows that his life is interlinked with his father's. But instead of accepting his fate and joining the Sith, Luke chooses to use his connection with Darth Vader to bring his father back to the light side of the Force.

ARE YOU ON A PATH TO THE DARK SIDE?

Every decision has a consequence. Qui-Gon agreed to train Anakin as a Jedi. Anakin gave in to his anger and destroyed Darth Tyranus. Mace Windu believed Anakin was loyal to the Jedi Order. Luke refused to give up faith in his father. A single moment is all it takes to choose between the light side and the dark side. Now, the choice is yours: which path will you take?

START HERE

ARE YOU ABLE TO CONTROL YOUR EMOTIONS?

YES

IS FRIENDSHIP MORE IMPORTANT THAN SUCCESS?

NO

NO

IS STRENGTH BETTER THAN INTELLIGENCE?

NO

WOULD YOU TRY TO NEGOTIATE BEFORE ENTERING A BATTLE?

YES

DO YOU EVER GO BACK ON YOUR WORD?

NO

YES

DO YOU VALUE POWER MORE THAN JUSTICE?

NO

YES

JEDI

You are brave and selfless enough to defend the galaxy from evil! Stay strong—and beware the Sith.

SENATOR

You have the chance to make a real difference in the galaxy through discussion and cooperation. Make sure you do not become greedy under the influence of others.

YES

BOUNTY HUNTER

You always look out for yourself—and will be very rich. Just be careful who you choose to work for.

NO

NO

SITH

You are strong and ambitious. You have chosen to seek power at all costs. But remember, the dark side will change you into something horrible.

DO YOU CRAVE POWER MORE THAN RICHES?

YES

HOW CAN A SITH LORD "BRING BALANCE TO THE FORCE"?

DARTH VADER HAS spent years trying to turn his son Luke Skywalker to the dark side. When he finally escorts a willing Luke to the Emperor's Throne Room, it seems the Sith Lord has succeeded. However, when Luke bravely resists the Emperor and faces his wrath, Darth Vader begins to question his own allegiance to the Sith.

FAITH IN HIS FATHER

When Luke refuses to join the dark side, the Emperor attacks him with deadly Sith lightning. In agony, Luke calls out to Darth Vader, begging for help. After all these years, Luke still believes there is good in his father.

MAKING A CHOICE

Hearing the desperate cries of his son, Vader finally turns against his Master, who has manipulated and controlled him for many years. He lifts the Emperor off his feet, saving Luke's life. Vader uses all his strength and willpower to throw Sidious into the Death Star's reactor core, where the Sith Lord is destroyed in a blast of Force energy.

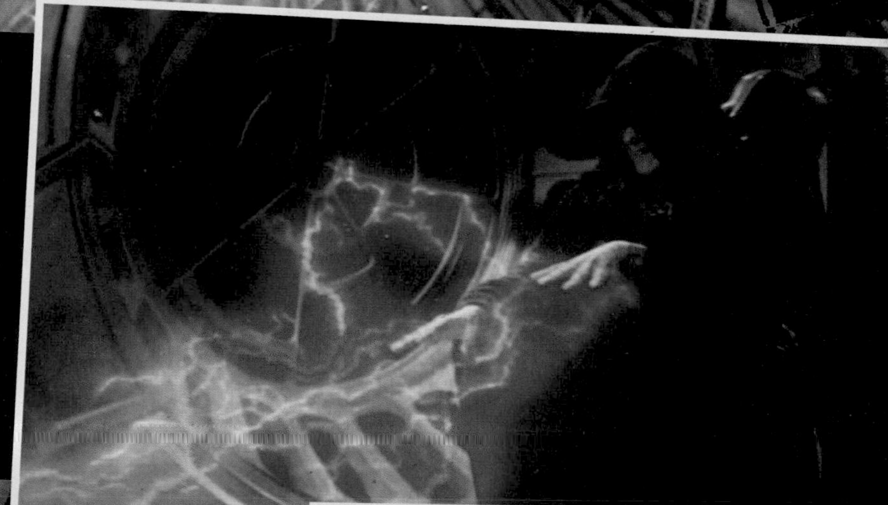

REDEMPTION

Anakin Skywalker returns to the light side of the Force, restoring the balance he destroyed by becoming a Sith 23 years earlier. The Emperor has been defeated and the Jedi Order is saved: the galaxy is free once more.

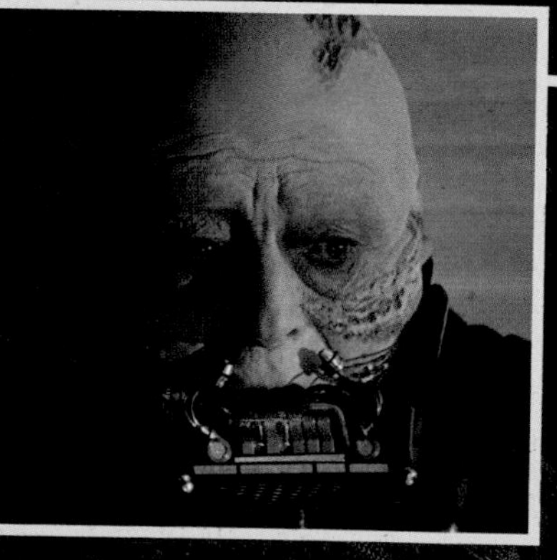

THE END OF THE SITH

When Anakin destroys Darth Sidious and returns to the light side of the Force, the Sith are finally destroyed. Although Anakin will not survive, he has succeeded in bringing balance to the Force... for now.

IS THIS THE END?

Darth Vader has once again become Anakin Skywalker. Emperor Palpatine has been destroyed. The Death Star has exploded into a billion pieces. As citizens of the galaxy celebrate and the Rebels and Jedi heroes reunite, it looks as if the Sith have been defeated once and for all. But the Sith are known to be sneaky. They survived undetected for over 1,000 years. Are they really gone for good?

SURVIVAL OF THE JEDI ORDER

Luke's courage and determination enabled him to destroy Darth Sidious's evil plans. The Jedi Order will continue, training new Jedi Knights and seeking peace and justice. Should danger ever return, the galaxy will be safe in the hands of the noble Jedi Order.

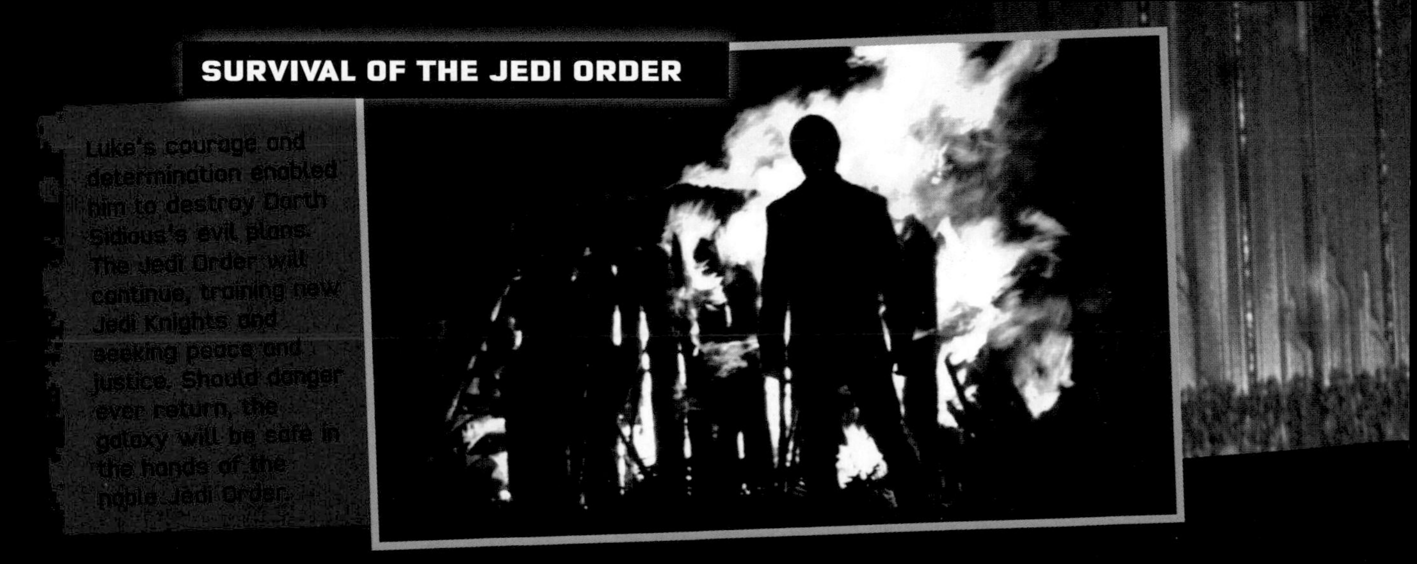

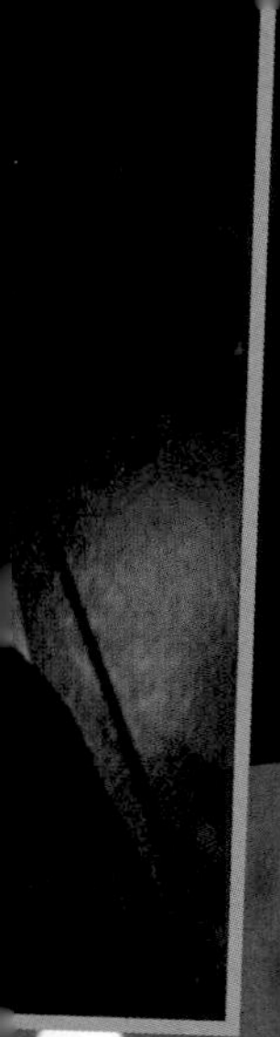

AT ONE WITH THE FORCE

Anakin joins Yoda and Obi-Wan Kenobi as Force spirits. Their life energies are able to survive after death, living on through the Force to offer guidance to future Jedi.

FREEDOM FOR THE GALAXY

With the collapse of the feared Empire, the galaxy is free once more. Almost every planet celebrates the victory, thankful they are no longer living under the Emperor's rule.

GLOSSARY

ALDERAAN
■ A peaceful planet, known for its beauty and culture, located in the Core Worlds.

ASTROMECH DROID
■ A utility robot that repairs and helps navigate starships.

BATTLE OF YAVIN
■ Conflict in Year 0 where Rebel forces, based on the moon Yavin 4, attacked and destroyed the first Imperial Death Star.

BOUNTY HUNTER
■ Someone who tracks down, captures, or kills wanted people in exchange for money.

CHANCELLOR
■ The title given to the head of the Galactic Senate and Republic.

CLONE ARMY
■ An army of genetically identical soldiers, all trained to be perfect warriors. They fight for the Republic.

CLONE WARS
■ A series of galaxy-wide battles fought between the Republic's Clone Army and the Droid Army of the Separatists, which took place between 22–19 BBY.

CORUSCANT
■ The capital of the Republic. This planet is home to the Senate building, the Jedi Temple, and the Jedi Council.

CYBORG
■ A being that is partly a living organism and partly a robot.

DARK SIDE
■ The evil side of the Force that feeds off negative emotions and offers raw power to those who study it.

DEATH STAR
■ A planet-sized Imperial battle station, which has enough firepower to destroy an entire planet.

DEMOCRACY
■ A system of government where all senior politicians are elected by the population.

DICTATORSHIP
■ An oppressive government whose leader wants complete control over everyone.

EMPEROR
■ Ruler of the Empire.

EMPIRE
■ An oppressive power that ruled the galaxy from 19 BBY to 4 ABY under the leadership of Emperor Palpatine, a Sith Lord.

FORCE
■ The energy that flows through all living things, which can be used for either good or evil.

GEONOSIS
■ A rocky, desert planet in the Outer Rim Territories, famous for its droid factories.

HOLOCRON
■ An ancient device, activated through use of the Force, that contains large amounts of data.

HOTH
■ An ice-covered planet located in a remote sector of the Outer Rim Territories.

JEDI
■ A member of the Jedi Order who studies the light side of the Force.

JEDI COUNCIL
■ The 12 senior, respected members of the Jedi Order who meet to make important decisions and give advice.

JEDI KNIGHT

■ A member of the Jedi Order who has studied as a Padawan under a Jedi Master and who has passed the Jedi Trials.

JEDI MASTER

■ A rank for Jedi Knights who have performed an exceptional deed or have trained a Jedi Knight.

JEDI ORDER

■ An ancient organization that promotes peace and justice throughout the galaxy.

JEDI PURGE

■ The attempt by Chancellor Palpatine in 19 BBY to annihilate the entire Jedi Order.

JEDI TEMPLE

■ The headquarters of the Jedi Order, located on the planet Coruscant.

LIGHTSABER

■ A weapon with a blade of pure energy that is used by Jedi and Sith warriors.

MUSTAFAR

■ A volcanic planet in the Outer Rim Territories, home to the Separatist Council at the end of the Clone Wars.

NABOO

■ A beautiful planet near the border of the Outer Rim Territories.

NEIMOIDIAN

■ A humanoid species native to the planet Neimoidia.

ORDER 66

■ An order given by Chancellor Palpatine that began the Jedi Purge. Every clone trooper in the Clone Army was ordered to kill all members of the Jedi Order.

PADAWAN

■ A Youngling who is chosen to serve an apprenticeship with a Jedi Master.

PROBE DROID

■ Imperial robot that gathers and transmits data.

REBEL ALLIANCE

■ The organization that resists and fights against the Empire.

REPUBLIC

■ The democratic government of the galaxy, under leadership of an elected Chancellor.

SENATE

■ Government of the Republic, with representatives from all parts of the galaxy.

SENATOR

■ A person who represents their planet, sector, or system in the Senate.

SEPARATISTS

■ An alliance against the Republic. Also known as the Confederacy of Independent Systems.

SITH APPRENTICE

■ A member of the Sith Order who has been selected for training by a Sith Master.

SITH LIGHTNING

■ Deadly rays of blue energy that can be used as a weapon by someone who has embraced the dark side of the Force.

SITH ORDER

■ An ancient sect of Force-sensitives who study the dark side to gain control and succeed in their greedy plans.

SITH CODE

■ A set of values and ancient teachings that guide the decisions of the members of the Sith Order.

SITH MASTER

■ A member of the Sith Order who passes on his knowledge of the dark side to an apprentice.

TATOOINE

■ A desert planet with two suns located in the Outer Rim Territories. Known as a meeting place for criminals and smugglers.

TRADE FEDERATION

■ A bureaucratic organization that controls much of the trade and commerce in the galaxy.

YOUNGLING

■ A Force-sensitive child who joins the Jedi Order to be trained in the Jedi arts.

INDEX

Characters are listed under their most frequently used common name, for example Luke Skywalker is found under "L" and "Count Dooku" is under "C."

A

B

C

D

E

F

G

H

I

J

K

L

T

V

X

Y

Z

LONDON, NEW YORK, MELBOURNE,
MUNICH, AND DELHI

For Dorling Kindersley

Editors Shari Last, Julia March, Helen Murray
Designers Clive Savage, Toby Truphet, Lynne Moulding, Rhys Thomas
Design Manager Ron Stobbart
Managing Editor Laura Gilbert
Art Director Lisa Lanzarini
Publishing Director Simon Beecroft
Publishing Manager Julie Ferris

Project Manager Sarah Harland
DTP Designer Kavita Varma
Senior Editor Tori Kosara
Senior Producer Verity Powell

For Lucasfilm
Executive Editor J. W. Rinzler
Art Director Troy Alders
Keeper of the Holocron Leland Chee
Director of Publishing Carol Roeder

This edition published in 2014
First published in the United States in 2012 by DK Publishing
345 Hudson Street, New York, New York 10014

First published as two separate titles: Star Wars®: *Mysteries of the Jedi* (2011), Star Wars®: *Beware the Sith* (2012)

001–270708—Sep/14

A catalog record for this book is available from the Library of Congress.

ISBN: 978-1-4654-2636-9

Color reproduction by Media Development Printing Ltd, UK
Printed and bound by Leo Paper Products Ltd., China

The publisher would like to thank Neil Ellis for his artwork on pages 134–135 and Alastair Dougall for his editorial assistance.

Discover more at
www.dk.com
www.starwars.com